BAUDELAIRE TO BECKETT

A Century of French Art & Literature

A Catalogue of Books, Manuscripts, and Related Material Drawn from
The Collections of the Humanities Research Center

SELECTED AND DESCRIBED BY CARLTON LAKE

Humanities Research Center · The University of Texas at Austin

Title page: Illustration by Odilon Redon. See entry no. 53.

FOREWORD

The great strengths of the research collections in modern English and American literature at The University of Texas at Austin are now common knowledge on both sides of the Atlantic. Less well known, less extensive, but no less noteworthy, the Texas modern-French collections complement the English-language materials in useful and enlightening ways. They are, of course, first of all, their own justification. But they have a central importance in relation to much else that is here, as evidence of the uniquely pervasive influence of the French on other cultures, an influence that no other modern literature has exerted quite so widely.

Since art and literature grow only partly out of life and in good measure from other art and other literature, it is a rare writer who has no traceable ancestors. And for many of the best modern American and British writers, the dominant ancestors have often been French. Yeats went so far as to say that ever since the time of Chaucer, "it is from France that nearly all the great influences in art and literature have come."

If one enjoys Wallace Stevens's poetry, one can enjoy it even more by perceiving in it reflections of Baudelaire, Verlaine, Laforgue, Mallarmé, and Valéry. In many respects, E. E. Cummings is an American phenomenon—and an original, to boot. And yet . . . one does situate him more accurately by reading him with a knowledge of the earlier innovations of Pierre Albert-Birot and Apollinaire, Dada and *391*, Mallarmé's *Un Coup de dés jamais n'abolira le hasard*, and the Cubist techniques—simultaneity, displacement, fragmentation—involved in the radical reorganization of the picture surface.

In the case of Henry Miller, one does not diminish the interest of his work by recognizing him as the spiritual godson of Cendrars and Céline. And Ezra Pound obviously meant to praise Joyce by calling him Flaubert's heir and saying that Joyce was the one who had best understood the lesson of *Bouvard et Pécuchet*. For that matter, can we really know Pound, or Eliot either, without knowing what they drew from the French—Pound from Remy de Gourmont, for example, and Eliot from Laforgue and Baudelaire, among others?

3

In another direction, has any twentieth-century literary movement been more variously influential than Surrealism? And theatre everywhere will be paying interest for years to come on its debt to the likes of Jarry, Artaud, Genet, Ionesco, and Beckett. The list is long.

But all this is as it should be. Just as French painting nourished us for nearly a century, so now American painting, in turn, nourishes the French, to the great enrichment of French pictorial tradition. In art, in literature, it is not simply—as elsewhere—that we cannot *afford* to erect national boundaries. It just can't be done.

Perhaps a word should be said about the slightly elastic interpretation given to the word "French" in the catalogue's subtitle. Joining hands with bona-fide Frenchmen we have Swiss, Belgians, Romanians, a Spaniard, a Hungarian, a Bulgarian, a very-probably-Italo-Pole, an Irishman, and even one American—Gertrude Stein, who, writing in French to and otherwise involved with a young French poet, refused on principle to be excluded from this consideration of Paris arts and letters. But this, too, is as it should be. For somehow the arts belong to France and France belongs to everybody—indeed is (to borrow the term Gertrude Stein applied to Susan B. Anthony) the mother of us all. And that brings us back to Yeats.

No attempt has been made here to present a systematic view of recent French literary history. The catalogue is simply an alphabetical journey, somewhat *en zigzag*, through a sampling of the French materials available in Austin. If it suggests new possibilities for research in French—and comparative—literature and, now and again, in the occasionally interweaving areas of painting, music, and some of the other arts, it will have achieved its purpose.

CARLTON LAKE

JE PRENDS PLAISIR
A M'ÉTENDRE SUR TOI
MAIS
JE SUIS SI LÉGÈRE MA
BIEN-AIMÉE ET MON
BLEU
VA SI BIEN
A TON
BLANC
TOUS LES AMANTS SONT JALOUX
DE LA DOUCEUR DES CARESSES
QUE JE TE FAIS ET L'ARBRE AUQUEL J'APPARTIENS
POUR L'ÉTERNITÉ
QUE DIRAIT-IL S'IL SAVAIT
NOTRE AMOUR IL N'Y A QUE LES
PEINTRES ET LES POÈTES
QUI SOIENT HEUR
DE VOIR NOS BAISERS
EUX DENTELÉS
LES HOMMES MARCHENT
DESSUS

AUSSI LONGUE QUE LA ROUTE

P. ALBERT-BIROT 1918

1

PIERRE ALBERT-BIROT

In January 1916, three full years before Dada installed itself officially and noisily at the center of the Paris avant-garde, and a year before the appearance of Pierre Reverdy's magazine, *Nord-Sud*, Albert-Birot founded the review *SIC* (*Son, Idées, Couleurs*).[1] It ran for exactly four years, then stopped before it ran down. In addition to Albert-Birot (painter, sculptor, poet, cabinetmaker, scholar, and avid seeker of the new), *SIC* published Apollinaire, Aragon, Breton, Cendrars, Cocteau, Dermée, Roch Grey, Max Jacob, Picabia, Radiguet, Salmon, Soupault, Tzara, and a host of others.

Like Guillaume Apollinaire, Albert-Birot was an ingenious practitioner of the *calligramme*, which has a long history in French literature, through Mallarmé all the way back to Rabelais and beyond.

"I walked across Futurism, Cubism, Dadaism, but I am neither futurist nor cubist, dadaist nor surrealist," Albert-Birot wrote in 1928. Apollinaire wrote of him:

> Pierre Albert-Birot is a kind of pyrogen,
> If you want to light some matches
>   Scratch them on him
>   They'll probably flare up
>   Too few pyrogens today
> I'll say nothing about matches.

Poèmepréfaceprophétie (1917).

Albert-Birot might have been summing up his own work when he wrote:

> Copy copy
> Religiously
> The Truth that you are
> And you'll make a poem
>
> Provided you're a poet.

1. *Je prends plaisir à m'étendre sur toi* . . . . Holograph manuscript signed,

[1] Cf. Baudelaire:
  Comme de longs échos qui de loin se confondent . . . .
  Les parfums, les couleurs et les sons se répondent.

7

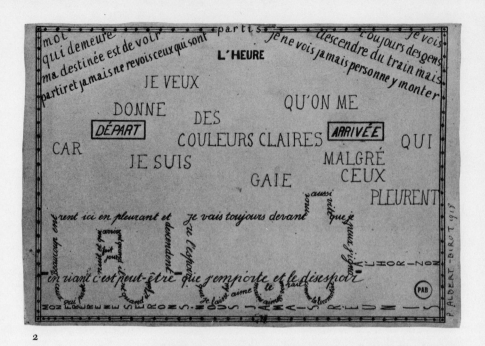

2

5

1918, 1 p. Folio. A *poème-paysage* published first in the review *SIC* (No. 47–48, June 1919) and, later that year, in *La Joie des sept couleurs*.

2. *Je veux qu'on me donne des couleurs claires* . . . . Holograph manuscript signed, 1918, 1 p. Oblong folio. *Poème-paysage* published in *La Joie des sept couleurs* (1919).

3. *Poèmes à l'autre moi*. [Paris] Les Éditions Jeanne Bucher, 1927. 4to, original wrappers, uncut.

First edition. One of 110 numbered copies on *vélin pur fil*. Inscribed on the half-title:

A Madame Otto Rank / si sympathique / avec tous mes souhaits les meilleurs / pour l'année 1935 et toutes / les autres / Paris Janvier 1935 / Pierre Albert-Birot.

4. *Grabinoulor. Épopée*. [Paris] Denoël et Steele [1933]. 8vo, original wrappers, uncut.

First edition. (The first section had been published in 1921 under the title *Le Premier livre de Grabinoulor*.) One of 5 numbered copies (No. 2) on *papier du Japon* of a total edition of 1,840. With the following inscription:

Pour Madame Otto Rank / à qui, certainement, sur ce / livre, toute dédicace, autre / que celle-ci, paraîtrait / banale / Pierre Albert-Birot.

JEAN ANOUILH

5. 77 holograph letters and postcards, signed, 1934–1939, to the playwright Léopold Marchand (see COLETTE, nos. 147, 149).

Detailed discussion of his plays and projects of the period, his health, and other personal difficulties. He writes of earlier playwrights who have interested him: Molière, Racine, Marivaux, Musset. In contrast to these masters, the contemporary theatre is overinflated with conversation:

. . . In my concept of the theatre I don't want—in the interest of realism—to begin a scene in which the audience has to learn something through talk about green peas or racehorses. I think social life has done a lot of harm to playwrights. All that chatter is such a bore in the work of those who won't resign themselves to saying only what is necessary.

GUILLAUME APOLLINAIRE

6. *L'Enchanteur pourrissant*. Paris: Henry Kahnweiler [1909]. 8vo, loose in sheets, uncut.

Proofs of the title-page, five pages of text, and 12 of Derain's original wood engravings, for the first edition, which was limited to 106 copies. Accompanying the proofs is Derain's original wash drawing for the title-page vignette, which the picture dealer D.-H. Kahnweiler used, beginning with this book, as his publishing emblem. It measures 6⅜″ x 8⅞″, is signed with the artist's initials, and bears instructions for the printer.

L'Enchanteur pourrissant, one of the milestones of twentieth-century book-making, was the first book Kahnweiler published, as well as the first book illustrated by Derain with original engravings. Derain's illustrations reflect the new interest in African sculpture, of which he was one of the earliest partisans, and were influential in redirecting the course of woodcut illustration. A few months before publication, Apollinaire, with characteristic ebullience, compared the book, in an anonymous prospectus, to the *Hypnerotomachia Poliphili*.

7. *Les Peintres cubistes. Méditations esthétiques. Ouvrage accompagné de 46 portraits et reproductions hors texte. Première série. Pablo Picasso–Georges Braque–Jean Metzinger–Albert Gleizes–Juan Gris–Mlle. Marie Laurencin–Fernand Léger–Francis Picabia–Marcel Duchamp–Duchamp-Villon, etc.* Paris: Eugène Figuière et Cie., 1913. 4to, original wrappers, uncut and unopened.

First edition. A fine copy, without the usual mention on the front cover of second, third, or other (imaginary) edition, for publicity purposes.

Apollinaire had wanted to call the book *Les Peintres nouveaux*, a more reasonable title, but the publisher, as publishers will, imposed what seemed to him a more dramatic—and saleable—one, however imprecisely it corresponded to the actual contents. The book owes a good deal to the painter Robert Delaunay, and to some extent grew out of the frequent discussions Apollinaire had with him, in his studio, about painting and painters. Delaunay doesn't appear in the book because Apollinaire had planned to bring out a second volume devoted largely to him. Apollinaire believed, as did Albert Gleizes, that Delaunay was one of the great ones.

The generous amount of space devoted here to Picabia's painting—even more than to Braque or Juan Gris—must be balanced against the fact that Picabia, affluent and free-spending, paid for the book's publication. Neither Picabia nor Apollinaire, in fact, had much interest in each other's work but they shared a kind of free-wheeling attitude toward life and art that made them enjoy each other's company.

8. *Le Poète assassiné*. Paris: Bibliothèque des Curieux, 1916. 12mo, full black morocco, gilt borders, top edges gilt, original pictorial wrappers bound in, uncut (binding by Bayntun).

First edition. The longest story in the collection, which gave the book its title, was originally planned as a novel. It is to a large degree autobiographical.

9. *Le Poète assassiné*. Complete set of page proofs of the first edition, corrected by Apollinaire. 4to, mounted on larger sheets and bound in one volume. Wrappers from the edition illustrated by Raoul Dufy have been bound in. Laid in is a letter from the book's publisher authenticating the proofs and the corrections.

6

9

10. *Les Mamelles de Tirésias. Drame surréaliste en deux actes et un pro-*
logue. Avec la musique de Germaine Albert-Birot et sept dessins hors-texte
de Serge Férat. Paris: Éditions *SIC*, 1918. In an intricately fashioned binding
of two-toned brown textured calf, with a cubist pattern formed of inlays of
wood, cork, brass, and a cardboard trellis effect beneath which are tiny
squares of red and mauve calf; doublures of beige calf, end-leaves of matching suede, all edges gilt, original wrappers bound in, uncut, within double
slipcase (binding by Leroux).

First edition of the celebrated play by Apollinaire in which the word "surrealist"
appeared for the first time. The play speaks topically to our own time through
its themes of the liberation of woman, population control (or decontrol), and
transsexualism. This copy belonged to Pierre Albert-Birot, who produced the play
and published it as well. It is inscribed:

A Pierre Albert-Birot / très cordial souvenir de son / ami / Guillaume
Apollinaire.

In a second volume, of larger format, in a matching half-binding, are bound
the following documents relating to the play and its production:

10

* Holograph letter signed from Apollinaire to Albert-Birot concerning production problems. Apollinaire encloses a clipping proving that the central character's use of rubber breasts (Louise Marion's blue and red balloons) is perfectly legal.

* Holograph letter signed from Apollinaire to Albert-Birot, 2 pp., on stationery of the Ministry of War, asking him to pass by and pick up the manuscript of *Les Mamelles de Tirésias*, to sign the contract, and to bring back drawings by Picasso and Matisse (which were used for the program).

* Holograph letter signed from Apollinaire to Albert-Birot, asking him to take 4 copies of *Les Mamelles* to the picture dealer Berthe Weill, and to let him know when that has been done so he may go to her gallery and sign them, as she has asked.

* Holograph note from Apollinaire to Albert-Birot, concerning some of the press notices.

* A subscription bulletin for the edition.

* Holograph manuscript draft for the subscription bulletin, in the hand of Albert-Birot.

* The printer's detailed bill for the invitation cards and the programs.

* Receipt made out to "Monsieur Guillaume Apollinaire" for 13 francs for the copyright on the work; on the bill-head of the Cercle de la Librairie.

* 2 holograph letters signed to Monsieur and Madame Pierre Albert-Birot from Renée Maubel, at whose Conservatoire the play was produced, concerning the use of her hall.

* Receipt on the letterhead of the Conservatoire Renée Maubel for 100 francs paid by Albert-Birot as a deposit on the rental of the hall.

* Another receipt, for the total amount paid (132 francs).

* Program for a later production of this work, together with Erik Satie's *Socrate* and Ribemont-Dessaignes's Dada play *Le Serin muet*.

* Holograph letter signed from the collector Jacques Doucet to Albert-Birot asking for information about the production date and price of the seats for "Guillaume Apollinaire's play."

* Holograph note on his carte-de-visite from the critic Fernand Divoire asking for 2 invitations for *Les Mamelles*.

* Holograph letter signed, from Sylvia Beach to Albert-Birot, 2 pp., asking for 2 invitations.

* Invitation for the première of the play.

* Pen-and-ink sketch in the hand of Albert-Birot for a coupon good for one program.

* Holograph letter signed from the actress Louise Marion (who played Thérèse-Tirésias) to Albert-Birot asking that Apollinaire not be present at the first rehearsal.

* Autograph note (in two hands, one that of Albert-Birot) concerning the crowds at the première, the lack of programs, the necessity of closing the doors and keeping out some who would have liked to see the play.

* The pink wrap-around band, with two critics' praises, issued, after the performance, to publicize the book.

* Holograph manuscript signed by Georges Gabory, 1 p. Folio. "Au lendemain des Mamelles de Tirésias / poème suppliant / à Guillaume Apollinaire."

* Proofs of the article which appeared in *SIC* following the play's production, 5 pp. 4to. With many corrections in the hand of Apollinaire, and with one addition in the hand of Albert-Birot.

* Holograph letter signed from the artist Léopold Survage to Albert-Birot concerning one of his drawings.

* 5 holograph letters signed from the actor Marcel Herrand (who played Thérèse's husband), mostly concerning the play.

* Holograph letter signed from the poet Paul Dermée to M. and Mme. Albert-Birot, 2 pp. Concerning the play and its rehearsals.

* Holograph manuscript in the hand of Albert-Birot for the table of contents of the special Apollinaire number of his review, *SIC*.

Albert-Birot tells in his *Poème anecdotique pour servir à l'histoire de notre temps* that Apollinaire told him in July 1916 that his play was ready but that he just needed to "tune it up." The tuneup dragged on, week after week, until, on the first day of spring, 1917, Apollinaire read him the first act. From then on it was nip and tuck until the première on 24 June.

Apollinaire claimed that he had written *Les Mamelles* as early as 1903 (elsewhere 1904). If so, he had rewritten it very extensively not long before its production. There are references to the war, to Picasso, Braque, and the Ballets Russes. Current and recent art and literary movements—Cubism, Futurism, Dada—had all left their mark on the play and its production. Appropriately enough, for a play clearly influenced by the work of Alfred Jarry, the audience was noisy and disorderly and most reviews were unfavorable. (Apollinaire himself found resonances in it of Plautus, Beaumarchais, and Goethe.)

11. Holograph manuscript draft for the original title-page of *Les Mamelles de Tirésias*, in which it is defined as a "drame surnaturaliste"[2] rather than "surréaliste," to which Apollinaire later changed it at the suggestion of Albert-Birot.

Apollinaire had been preoccupied with the idea of the "supernatural" for some

[2] In his *Salon de 1846*, Baudelaire had written of the "surnaturalisme" of Delacroix, as Apollinaire, in all likelihood, would have known.

time. In the 1912 Salon des Indépendants Chagall had exhibited the painting now known as *Dedicated to My Fiancée* (Kunstmuseum, Berne), but then listed as *La Lampe et les deux personnes*. Apollinaire cited it as one of the "significant" works in the show. The following year he visited Chagall in his studio at La Ruche, and after looking at his paintings, applied to them the term "sur-naturel." "Keep right on," he told Chagall, "you have a talent that marks you for attention." It was then that Chagall, grateful for the enthusiastic support of the man he later referred to as "that gentle Zeus," reciprocated by giving to his large allegorical painting of Adam and Eve— his most important work to date—the title *Homage to Apollinaire* (Stedelijk van Abbe-Museum, Eindhoven).

12. Prologue for *Les Mamelles de Tirésias*. Holograph manuscript with several small pen-and-ink sketches, 8 pp. Small 4to, cloth-backed boards. Extensive corrections. The prologue was written as plans for the play's production were going forward.

13. Manuscript copy, in Apollinaire's hand, of an article by Léo Poldès in *La Grimace*, 1 p. Folio. The article ridicules *Les Mamelles de Tirésias*, and closes with the line, "Ah! les cochons!"

14. Subscription form and pink publicity band for *Les Mamelles* and invitation to the première.

15. *Les Mamelles de Tirésias. Avec six portraits inédits par Picasso*. Paris: Éditions du Bélier, 1946. Square 12mo, three·quarter morocco, top edges gilt, original wrapper bound in, uncut.

> First edition with the Picasso sketches. One of 440 numbered copies on *vélin teinté Malacca des papeteries de Lana*. Daragnès bookplate.

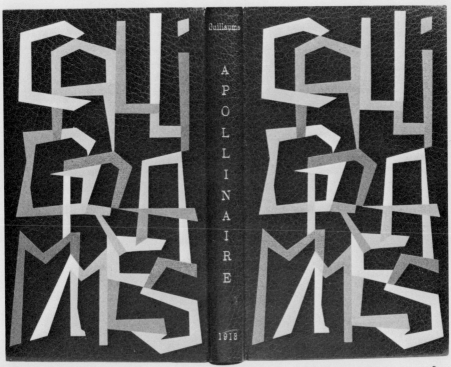

16. Holograph letter signed to "Lou" [Louise de Coligny-Châtillon, inspiration of the poems published in *Ombre de mon amour*], "18 Avril 1915," 2 pp. Includes the 32-line poem beginning "Mon Lou, ma chérie, je t'envoie aujourd'hui la première pervenche . . ."

17. Holograph letter signed to Jean Mollet [the "Baron" Mollet, who served as Apollinaire's secretary], "28 Avril 1915," 2 pp. Written from the front. "Ici on est sur la ligne de feu . . . Théâtre de la guerre, on joue Obus Roi . . ."

18. *Calligrammes. Poèmes de la paix et de la guerre (1913–1916) . . . . Avec un portrait de l'auteur par Pablo Picasso . . . .* Paris: Mercure de France, 1918. 8vo, brown crushed levant with inlays in six colors of paper forming intersecting letters which spell out the book's title, top edges gilt, original wrappers bound in, uncut, in slipcase (binding by Devauchelle). First edition.

19. *Calligrammes. Lithos de Chirico.* Paris: nrf [Nouvelle Revue Française], 1930. 4to, loose in sheets in original wrappers, uncut, within decorative slipcase, as issued.

> This edition of *Calligrammes*, one of the rarest of modern French illustrated books, was limited to 100 copies: 4 on Whatman paper, 6 on *Japon nacré*, and 90 on China paper, designed by Maurice Darantière, the celebrated printer of Joyce's *Ulysses*, and printed in three colors under his direction. The original lithographs were drawn directly on the stone by Giorgio de Chirico.
>
> This copy, No. 1 of the 4 on Whatman paper, is from the library of Maurice Darantière, and bears his bookplate. It is signed on the limitation page in pencil by Chirico. Some signatures are present in proof state, and some have Darantière's markings. Laid in are two variant forms of the original prospectus, with subscription form.

20. *Calligrammes. Lithos de Chirico.* Paris: nrf [Nouvelle Revue Française], 1930. Another copy, one of the 6 on *Japon nacré*. From the library of Maurice Darantière, with his bookplate.

21. *L'Oeuvre du Marquis de Sade. Zoloé.—Justine / Juliette.—La Philosophie dans le boudoir / Les Crimes de l'Amour. Pages Choisies / Comprenant des morceaux inédits / et des lettres publiées pour la première fois, tirées des Archives / de la Comédie Française. Introduction, Essai Bibliographique et Notes par Guillaume Apollinaire. Ouvrage orné de trois Gravures et d'un Autographe hors texte.* Paris: Bibliothèque des Curieux, 1912. 8vo, original wrappers, uncut.

> The first of the series *Les Maîtres de l'Amour*, edited by Apollinaire. This copy belonged to Apollinaire's "Lou" and is inscribed in her hand, on the front free end-paper:
>
> *Ctesse Louise de Coligny*

C A L L I G R A M M E S

Fantassins
Marchantes mottes de terre

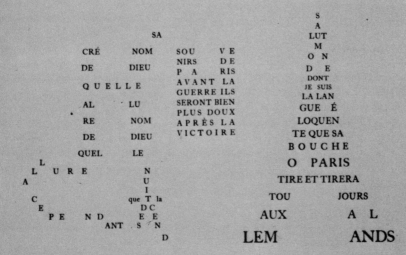

Vous êtes la puissance
Du sol qui vous a faits
Et c'est le sol qui va

90

22. *Hommage à Guillaume Apollinaire* by Blaise Cendrars. Proof corrected by Cendrars of his tribute to Apollinaire, printed on verso of a proof of the title-page of Roch Grey: "Gullaume [sic] Apollinaire," the first book about Apollinaire. Signed by Pierre Albert-Birot, who published the book.

23. *A Guillaume Apollinaire, mon ami* by Louise Faure-Favier. Holograph manuscript signed, 3 pp. Folio. This article, as well as Cendrars's poem, appeared in the special issue of *SIC* dedicated to the memory of Apollinaire.

25

Deux Décembre, Fort-Louis.

Vous vous décobez méchamment, ces prières. Voyez, je descendis, au moins les toiles. On seriez-vous jaloux de leur virginité? Je suis bien plus neuf que vous ne pouvez croire et c'est mal de refuser des morceaux d'ciel au premier qui voulait s'en faire une robe. Pour mettre le Dimanche, à la Messe du village.

Aiguilles de cire au flanc de la bougie, j'ai toché une lui pas blue: La pointe se flamme, il n'y forme une goutte transparente, chaude - chaude - elle tombe, une larme.

A Lise le chocolat dont le nom se lit en capitales, à la flamme bloe Bougie - la même - les lettres s'effacent et cette odeur de caramel.

Toute ma vie
J'habite un château près du Rhin, mais on n'a pas voulu le l'appeler burg. Il y a une vieille femme charmante te et les cafetiers portent, jolies boîtes serpentines. Dans les auberges il y a des bals, et la musique militaire pour que la Place de l'Eglise et cette histoire me me s'il n'y avait pas ailleurs un tapis de sable en velours rouge, l'encre rouge que personne ne lira jamais.

Et sans transition:
Vous posez le dilemme, se suicider ou vivre: fable, il y a des triangles qui ont leurs angles à gauche chacun, mais ils se peuvent coïncider, simples les allonger. Je suis un triangle beaucoup plus grand que la Norète 1918. Vous se dévelorergis en protestant. Mais ma loge n'écrirai pas, vous la nommez à l'idiote fini, est le villag d'avant Tebua, qu'en on s'approprait la scène se polige à Lavessarah: aujourd'hui même on n'a soufflé d'une bourgeria (l'oder des foins où fatalement s'attirent jouer avec une soirée inaperdent). Je suis loin qui ne huile avec aucun loup. Les voisins d'en face - le Rhin n'est pas si large, je suis la Cruelle de soleil. Moi Mol zurm drapeaux rouges. Mais voici je n'ai pas de drapeau et pas de bois ni compromission. les nuages, j'ai la terre pour pied à terre, appartient et je pouvai vai, et je Corse faire tomber dans les ruisseaux le long les flottais j'en aurais quelques-uns, mais je feuillent entonnent le sable vois l'eau avec les bâtons. Ce sont des compris rer pâtes en pâte d'inspection pour cela un VASE.

Ses plus jolies, images on me les a loué quand j'eus l'égale miroir
Songez que maintenant j'ai un le Masque de Fer. Cette lettre, pleut d'argent lancé par la fenêtre la facteur vous l'apportous lisez le un auqué avec la pointe d'incontourn (sur l'argent on ne peut pas écrire avec son sang)

Louis Aragon
Fort-Louis.

L/XII/18   30

24. Holograph letter signed from Maurice Vlaminck to the novelist Roland Dorgelès, "14 mars 1934," 2 pp., 4to. Recounts his last meeting with Apollinaire, six days before the poet's death.

25. *Portrait de Guillaume Apollinaire* by Jean Hugo. Pen-and-ink. Measures 5⅜″ x 4⅛″.   See also PABLO PICASSO, no. 345.

LOUIS ARAGON

26. *Le 24 Juin 1917*. Holograph manuscript signed, 2 pp. 4to. Aragon's account, written for the review *SIC*, of the opening of Apollinaire's play *Les Mamelles de Tirésias*.

After reviewing the details of that historic performance, Aragon sums up its importance: "I shall always keep, from that afternoon of 24 June, 1917, the memory of a unique gaiety which allows me to predict for the future a theatre liberated from the need to philosophize."

27. Holograph letter signed to Albert-Birot, 12 February 1918, calling his attention to a "stupid spelling error" in the preceding manuscript.

28. *Madame Tusseaud* [sic]. Holograph manuscript signed.

29. *Pur Jeudi*. Holograph manuscript signed.

30. 7 holograph letters signed to Jean Cocteau and 2 to Raymond Radiguet, 1918–1919, 15 pp.

An intimate and revealing group of letters, in which Aragon appears at his most beguiling. In one of the letters, Aragon, still in the service, urges Cocteau to watch his health. It's a bad season for poets; Apollinaire and Jacques Vaché have already died. There are hints of a quarrel between Aragon and Breton ("MY poet André . . . I am his public, understand . . . .") which none of the literature of the period would explain, but which is apparently related, in some measure, to Breton's hostility toward Cocteau. (Cocteau's *Le Cap de bonne espérance* had recently appeared and Breton hadn't liked it.) Four of the letters contain unpublished poems by Aragon.

From one of the letters addressed to Radiguet, whom Aragon met in March 1919, we learn that Radiguet had sent him two of his poems in manuscript. Aragon showed them to a number of his friends, all of whom liked them but apparently for the wrong reasons, and he takes Radiguet to task for occasionally showing the influence of Mallarmé. Other lines—annoyingly, for Aragon—make him think of Reverdy.

Aragon is a stern critic—he is 21, Radiguet 16—particularly when he cautions Radiguet to be on guard against "the literature of childhood, which has already been done by Rimbaud (*Une Saison en enfer*) . . . ."

"I'm glad to know you are thinking of the stage, even for a farce. Mr. Radiguet, playwright. You write French, and that is rare." See RAYMOND RADIGUET, no. 358.

31. 21 holograph letters and postcards, signed, plus 2 related documents, to his friends René Thomas and Annie Besnard, 1933–1940.

The longest and most moving of these letters were written in the fall of 1940 from Ville-Evrard, a grim institution where Artaud was confined from February 1939 to January 1943, and where his condition, mental and physical, deteriorated steadily.

The letters are filled with Artaud's accounts of satanic plots, demonic visitations, plans for escape and long, improbable voyages, infernal visions and hallucinations, and echoes of his sexual fears and obsessions.

There is always a final cavern of evil which opens up during my sleep, and those who come out of it, who, oddly, have been hidden until then, come up to me and force me to undergo one more horrible mutilation. And I get up like a man who has been battered. And it has been like that every morning for more than 450 days. I can't take any more of the suffering here. My torture must end . . . .

JACQUES AUDIBERTI

32. *La Fourmi dans le corps.* Holograph manuscript, 98 pp. Folio. Early draft with many corrections, in some places completely rewritten.

Audiberti generally rewrote his plays several times, setting down his drafts very rapidly, then going back and slowly and carefully making the many changes he brought to each draft. There are drawings scattered throughout the manuscript, and the names of certain real-life models that Audiberti had in mind during the play's development are noted.

This play, whose subject had been suggested to Audiberti by the poet Claude Lehmann, was first produced on French radio on 29 December 1960. After the radio première, Thérèse Marney decided that this was a role intended for her. As a result, Audiberti reworked the play, and it was taken into the repertory of the Comédie Française and performed there in 1962.

GEORGES AURIC

33. *Petite surprise de jour de l'an.* Holograph music manuscript signed and dated "Sorgues, ler septembre 1920." A birthday song for Irène Lagut, based on a poem by Jean Cocteau.

34. *La Symphonie pastorale. No. VII. Le Pasteur et Gertrude.* Holograph music manuscript signed, Paris 1946, 6 pp. Folio, plus title-page.

35. 47 holograph letters and postcards, signed, to the artist Jean Hugo and his wife Valentine [née Gross], 1918–1927; together with 8 pages of drawings

empêche de vous venger. Mais
pendant ce temps on vous enlève
vos forces, vos nerfs, votre vie
votre joie d'exister et si cela
continue vous allez bientôt vous
trouver aussi malade que moi
et je viens de cela à aucun
prix. Ça travaille de toutes mes
forces à réparer le mal mais
je n'ai plus de forces.
Comment les mutilés ont-ils afflige
je ne vois à distance de
nouveaux instruments de torture
sur ceux pour qui l'on applique
sont aussi réels je me rends
ou le jeu d'ostine, et je me vois
réveillé honteusement inutile et
le tête et les mains affreusement
broyés, et paralysé. Ma vie
n'est qu'une agonie. Il faut me
trouver de l'héroïne à tout
prix et par tous les moyens.
C'est très grave Anie, croyez-moi
je ne puis plus sortir si je n'ai pas
de l'héroïne avant —
Je vous embrasse
Antonin Artaud

31

2   Pie Saint Pép de m'avoir accompagné
                Je te remercie
           Dr Marquet   je quis continuer
6h! Mon le temps d'avaler un bouillon à l'heure de la
        cloche.
              enquise le pavé quatre
                        Pie Saint Pép   Je ne m'arrêterai pas
                                                     la poste
        te prendra.
              Dr Marquet
       Et les chevaux de selle   one!
              Pie Saint Pép
                              Mieux vaudrait que
        Caracole, toi?
        Je te transporte sur mon dos jusqu'à Paris
                              Reste
                              donc, va!
              Dr Marquet
        M'évanouir de cette contrée, (aimant
        un mouvement j'évitais) faisette la brumette
                                      dix davantage
        me tient à cœur, riz ce que me fait la
        guerre dans le canton que nous vaut le tic que
        d'éclater.
                        franchement, je surprennent
        autant que dans me   j'ai
        d'avance l'idée de m'expliquer au extrême.
              Pie Saint Pép
        Je suis chez moi. Je vous reçois.

32

38

39

by Auric in pencil, ink, colored crayon and gouache, and a one-page holograph music manuscript signed, *Revenez vite Valentine* [1922].

Valentine Hugo was an important link in the chain that brought and held together Picasso, Cocteau, Erik Satie, Misia Sert, and Diaghilev for the ballet *Parade* (1917), one of the century's creative landmarks. In the period that followed, she and her husband, Jean Hugo, great-grandson of Victor Hugo, were, along with Jean Cocteau, Raymond Radiguet, Auric, Francis Poulenc, and Darius Milhaud, at the center of one of the most artistically active and articulate groups in Paris. This correspondence documents those friendships and activities.

36. *La Musique. L'Enfant et les sortilèges.* Holograph manuscript signed, 2 pp. A review of Ravel's music and Colette's fable.

37. *La Musique. Isabelle et Pantalon.* Holograph manuscript signed, 2 pp. Folio. A review of an opéra-bouffe by Max Jacob and Roland-Manuel.

38. *La Musique.* Holograph manuscript signed, 8 pp. 8vo. The first page of the manuscript is written on a sheet of stationery from the Welcome Hotel at Villefranche, on the Riviera, headquarters of the Cocteau group at the period.

The manuscript is chiefly concerned with Auric's recollections of the "formidable explosive force" of Stravinsky's *Le Sacre du printemps*, as it burst on Paris in May 1913.

39. *Le Sacre du printemps. Tableaux de la Russie païenne en deux parties d'Igor Stravinsky et Nicolas Roerich* . . . [Leipzig] Édition Russe de Musique, 1913. Folio, original cloth-backed boards. First printing.

40. *Sonatine pour le Piano.* Paris: Rouart, Lerolle & Cie., 1923. Folio, original wrappers, uncut.

First printing. The piece is dedicated to Francis Poulenc. This copy bears the inscription:

A G. Jean-Aubry, / ce petit souvenir / — cordialement — / de / Georges Auric.

41. *Portrait of Georges Auric* by Jean Hugo. Pencil. 10¾" x 8¼".

42. *Portrait of Georges Auric* by Valentine Hugo. Pencil. 10¾" x 8¼". A preliminary study for her well-known lithographic portrait, below.

43. *Portrait of Georges Auric* by Valentine Hugo. Original lithograph. 10¼" x 8¼". Signed and dated (1921) in the stone.

44

44. 6 pen-and-ink sketches of Georges Auric by Jean Cocteau, from a group of 33 made in 1923. Each measures 10⅝″ x 8⅜″.

45. 10 photographs of Auric, 1 with Cocteau, 1 with Poulenc.

HONORÉ DE BALZAC

46. *Les Amours de deux bêtes*. Holograph manuscript, 5 pp. 4to. With corrected proofs, 23 pp. 4to and 8vo.

This tightly packed manuscript contains the first five chapters of a story from *Scènes de la vie privée et publique des animaux* (Hetzel, 1841–42). As he wrote, Balzac left a wide margin at the left, which he later filled with additions and corrections. During the writing Professor de Rungis became Professor Granarius; the setting, originally called Nopalie, became Cactriane; and there are many variants from the printed text.

The proofs, heavily corrected, cover the entire 11 chapters of the story except for Chapter 7 and small gaps elsewhere. The variants between these corrected proofs and the published version are explained by a note to the printer in Balzac's hand at the top of the first page: "Legendre, let me have by Monday evening proof in duplicate of this, carefully corrected, with a proof in duplicate of the ending, which I am adding in manuscript. Send it all to No. 28 rue du faubourg poissonnière. M. Hetzel is away."

spectacle dans les infiniment petits ne doit-il pas nous inspirer à nous... Le choléra-morbus n'est-il pas...

— Notre Volvoce! s'écria la jeune fille.

Le professeur renversa la table en courant embrasser son enfant.

— Ah! tu es au fait de la science à ce point, chère Annette? Tu n'épouseras qu'un savant! Volvoce! qui t'a dit ce mot!...

— Le prince! le prince...

— Le prince, reprit le vieux professeur en donnant un coup à sa perruque, a échappé, grâce à la sollicitude du gouvernement français, à ce fléau destructeur; mais on l'enlève, sans le consulter, à son beau pays, à son bel avenir, et avec d'autant plus de facilité que sa vie était un problème. Pour parler clairement, Jarpéado, le soixante-sept milliardimillionième de sa dynastie... [Et, fit le professeur entre parenthèse, en levant vers le plafond plein de Bêtes empaillées, sa mouillette trempée de café, vous faites les fiers, messieurs les Bourbons, les Othomans, races royales et souveraines, qui vivez à peine des quinze à seize siècles avec les mille et une précautions de la civilisation la plus raffinée... Ô combien...] Enfin Jarpéado ne se trouvait pas plus avancé dans l'échelle des êtres que ne l'est une Altesse Royale onze mois avant sa naissance, et il fut transporté sous cette forme, chez mon prédécesseur, l'illustre Lacrampe, inventeur des Canards, et qui achevait leur monographie alors que nous eûmes le malheur de le perdre;

mais il vivra tant que vivra la Peau de chagrin, où l'illustrateur l'a représenté Planchette à qui, pour la gloire de la science, a légué le soin de rechercher la configuration, l'étendue, la profondeur, les qualités des princes onze mois avant leur naissance Planchette soutient contre cet intrigant de Cuvier qu'ils devaient être infusoires, remuants, et déjà décorés. Le gouvernement français, sollicité par feu Lacrampe, s'en remit au fameux spéculateur pour l'enlèvement du prince Jarpaédo, qui, grâce à son état, put venir par mer du fond de la province de Guaxaca, sur un lit de pourpre composé de trois milliards environ de sujets de son père, embaumés par les Indiens qui, certes, valent le docteur Gannal comme les lois sur la traite ne concernent pas les morts, ces précieuses momies furent vendues à Bordeaux, pour servir aux plaisirs et aux jouissances de la race blanche, jusqu'à ce que le soleil, père les absorbât dans ses rayons... Oui, apprends, mon Anna, que pas une des nymphes de Rubens, pas une des jolies filles de Miéris, que pas un trompette de Wouwermans n'a pu se passer de ces peuplades il y a des populations entières dans ces belles lèvres qui vous souriait au Musée, ou qui vous défient. Oh! si, par un effet de magie, la vie était rendue aux êtres ainsi distillés, quel charmant spectacle que celui de la décomposition d'une vierge de Raphaël ou d'une bataille de Rubens Hélas! peut-être y a-t-il là-haut un peintre puissant qui prend ainsi l'humanité sur des palettes, et

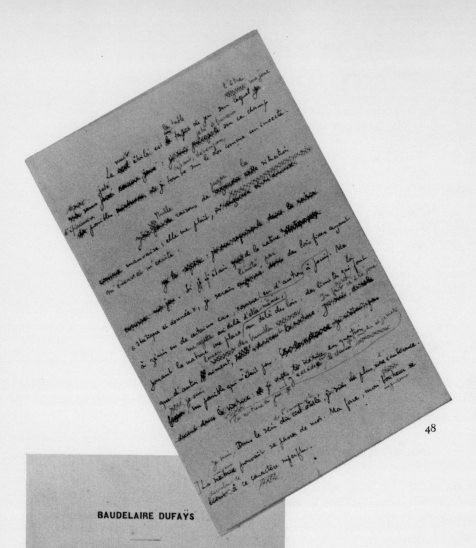

48

51

47. *L'Orestie*. Paris: Les Éditions des Quatre Vents, 1945. 8vo, original wrappers, uncut. First edition. One of 175 numbered copies on *papier teinté nacré*.

48. *L'Orestie*. Holograph manuscript, 58 pp. and title-page, bound in one volume. 8vo, full vellum. From the library of the poet Georges Hugnet, with his bookplate.

> The manuscript gives evidence of much rewriting, and large portions of the original text, here lightly deleted, do not appear in the printed version.

49. *Dianus*. [*Histoire de rats*. (*Journal de Dianus*).] Holograph manuscript, 90 pp. 8vo, tipped to mounts and bound in one volume, 8vo, full parchment, in slipcase. With the Georges Hugnet bookplate.

> La rédaction d'*Histoire de rats* et de *Dianus* est certainement postérieure à 1944, mais les manuscrits de ces deux textes, ou toute autre indication, nous manquent.
>
> Oeuvres Complètes de Georges Bataille
Vol. III, p. 509. [Paris] Gallimard (1971).

50. *Histoire de l'oeil*. Corrected typescript and corrected page proofs of the edition illustrated by Hans Bellmer.

CHARLES BAUDELAIRE

51. *Salon de 1846* by Baudelaire-Dufaÿs.[3] Paris: Michel Lévy Frères, 1846. 12mo, three-quarter crushed levant, original pink wrappers bound in, uncut (binding by Carayon).

> The rare first edition of the key book in Baudelaire's career as art critic. He had published his first *Salon* in 1845. It was an exploratory work but still fairly conventional. About the same time, Baudelaire met Delacroix, for whose work he had a boundless admiration, and Delacroix's ideas on painting had a significant effect on his own. The *Salon de 1846*, twice the length of the earlier volume, was surer, freer, richer. Although one catches in it occasional echoes of Diderot, Stendhal and, of course, Delacroix, it is clearly different from any other art criticism of the period. It marked Baudelaire at once as the most original critic of his time, and it bears the seeds of an aesthetic doctrine which seems today a primary source of the best in modern art criticism—a judgment amply confirmed by Baudelaire's *Salon de 1859* (not separately published).

52. *Les Fleurs du mal*. Paris: Poulet-Malassis et de Broise, 1857. 12mo, full gray-blue crushed levant with an intricate mosaic decorative pattern in vari-

---

[3] In publishing his first two books, Baudelaire used his mother's maiden name in combination with his family name. At the same period—and later—he used other variants of her name, the exact spelling of which has never been determined.

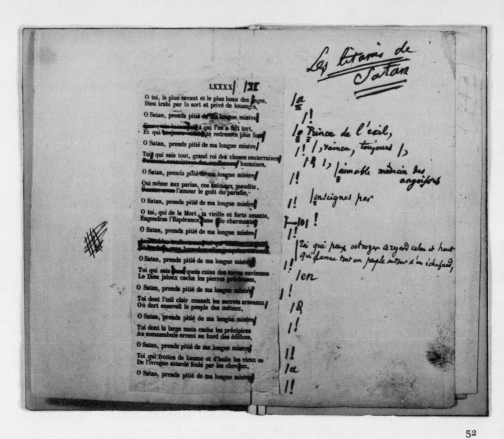

colored morocco inlays and gold-stamping, depicting, on the front cover, a design of passion flowers with a coiled serpent, all within a border of autumn leaves; on the back cover, an inlaid design of flowers growing from a skull, within a similar border; inlaid interior borders of poppies and marguerites, raised bands, all edges gilt (binding by Charles Meunier).

First edition of the most important nineteenth-century French book of poetry. This is a presentation copy, with the following inscription on the half-title, in ink and in Baudelaire's hand:

A mon ami Nadar. / Ch. Baudelaire.

Nadar (the pseudonym of Félix Tournachon), pioneer photographer, balloonist, writer, and caricaturist, met Baudelaire in about 1843 and was one of the very small inner circle of friends that included Théodore de Banville and Charles Asselineau. He made several of the finest photographic portrait studies we have of Baudelaire. His memoir, *Charles Baudelaire intime. Le Poète vierge*, was published in 1911.

This copy of *Les Fleurs du mal* has three autograph corrections in Baudelaire's hand, on pages 29, 110, and 217.

Bound in are the original proof sheets, from this edition, of one of the longest and most celebrated poems in the book—*Les Litanies de Satan*, which had not appeared in print before its publication in the book. The proofs show an earlier, otherwise unknown version of the poem. Baudelaire's corrections affect nearly every line, but the poem as corrected still shows certain substantial differences from the published version.

Bound in also are a holograph letter signed, with integral address leaf, from Baudelaire to the publisher, Auguste Poulet-Malassis, at Clichy prison; a holograph letter signed by Nadar, ending with the war-cry "Merde pour Vernet" (the painter Horace Vernet—"the antithesis of the artist"—was a frequent target of Baudelaire's criticism); and a holograph note signed from Poulet-Malassis to the critic Philippe Burty, a friend of Baudelaire's.

Bound in this copy is the series (before letters) of "interpretations" of *Les Fleurs du mal* by Odilon Redon, of which 80 sets were printed in this format on *papier vélin* for insertion in the book. Also bound in is a series of ten etchings by Alexandre Hannotiau to illustrate the book. Bound in as frontispiece is a color composition by Carlos Schwabe showing a demon dragging down a singing angel.

53. *Les Fleurs du mal. Interprétations par Odilon Redon.* Bruxelles: Chez Edmond Deman, 1891. 8vo, loose in sheets within original portfolio, with ties, as issued. One of 10 sets on Japan paper of Redon's interpretations of Baudelaire, which Deman commissioned as extra-illustrations for his edition of *Les Fleurs du mal.*

54. *La Charogne.* Holograph manuscript signed, 3 pp. Folio, written on two leaves (the second in two parts). Bound in full dark-blue levant, doublures and end-leaves of maroon levant, gilt fillets, all edges gilt (binding by P.-L. Martin).

One of the most disturbingly original poems of *Les Fleurs du mal*, characteristic of the book's *"frisson nouveau,"* and published in the first edition as *Une Charogne* (No. XXVII). In addition to the change of title the manuscript shows three variants from the published version.

This manuscript—lacking its final strophe and Baudelaire's signature—once belonged to Arthur Symons, whose critical writings and translations played a major role in bringing Baudelaire's work and that of the French symbolists to the English-speaking world. Some years later the last segment of the manuscript was reunited with Symons's portion, and the complete manuscript came into the collection of Jean Davray, whose bookplate the present binding bears.

55. *Charles Baudelaire intime. Le Poète vierge. Déposition–Documents–Notes–Anecdotes–Correspondances–Autographes et Dessins–Le Cénacle–La Fin* by Nadar. Paris: A. Blaizot, 1911. 8vo, three-quarter parchment, top edges gilt, original wrappers bound in.

One of 20 copies (No. 2) on Japan paper with an inscription from the publisher to the bibliophile Pierre Dauze. The edition was limited to 271 copies.

Étoile de mes yeux, soleil de ma nature
Vous, mon ange et ma passion,

Oui! telle vous serez, ô la reine des grâces,
Après les derniers sacrements,
Quand vous irez sous l'herbe et les floraisons
grasses,
Moisir parmi les ossements.

Alors, ô ma beauté! dites à la vermine
Qui vous mangera de baisers,
Que j'ai gardé la forme et l'essence divine
De mes amours décomposés!

Charles Baudelaire.

54

57

56. *Tous les hommes sont mortels. Roman.* [Paris] Gallimard (1946). 8vo, original wrappers, uncut. First edition of Beauvoir's third novel, dedicated to Jean-Paul Sartre. One of 55 numbered copies on *vélin pur fil.*

57. *Tous les hommes sont mortels.* Holograph manuscript and typescript, 640 pp. Folio and 4to. There are many long deletions and other changes throughout the manuscript; 38 of the pages are corrected typescript.

SAMUEL BECKETT

After World War II, in one of this century's most remarkable virtuoso performances, Beckett began writing in French, presumably to give himself the benefit of a precision instrument more appropriate to his needs. Between 1946 and 1950 his manuscripts were rejected by six Paris publishers before Jérôme Lindon, of Les Éditions de Minuit, decided to gamble on him. Lindon brought out *Molloy* at the end of 1951 and followed it shortly with *Malone meurt.* Beckett was enthusiastically accepted as a French writer by major French writers and critics—Maurice Nadeau, Maurice Blanchot, Georges Bataille, Alain Robbe-Grillet, among others.

The following year *En attendant Godot*, written in 1946, was published. In January 1953, Roger Blin, who had heard the play praised by Tristan Tzara three years earlier, produced it with the help of a state subsidy equivalent to about $1,500. Its success was immediate and—translated into more than twenty languages—international.

L'Innommable appeared in 1953. That year Beckett translated *En attendant Godot* into English and it was published as *Waiting for Godot* by Grove Press the year after. He began work also, in 1953, on the English versions of the novels. *Molloy* was published in English in 1955 by Olympia Press in Paris and by Grove Press in New York. Grove Press also published *Malone Dies* in 1956 and *The Unnamable* two years later.

58. *Malone meurt. Roman.* [Paris] Les Éditions de Minuit (1951). 12mo, original wrappers, uncut and unopened, in cloth folding case. First edition. Inscribed copy.

59. *L'Absent (Malone meurt).* Holograph manuscript signed, dated at beginning "27–11–47" and at end, "30 mai, 1948." In 2 folio notebooks, written on recto of 149 folio pages, with additions on facing blanks.

The notebook containing the beginning of the novel includes a substantial portion of the original manuscript of *Watt.*

60. *Malone Dies. A novel translated from the French by the author.* New York: Grove Press (1956). 8vo, original decorated wrappers. Inscribed by Beckett:

> *first edition of my / translation of Malone meurt . . .*

61. *Malone Dies.* Corrected carbon typescript, 159 pp. 4to, in cloth folding box. Inscribed, "Samuel Beckett / corrections in my hand / published by Grove Press— / N. Y. 1956."

62. *En attendant Godot. Pièce en deux actes.* [Paris] Les Éditions de Minuit, 1952. 12mo, original wrappers, uncut. First edition, inscribed:

> *for / Nancy [Cunard] / with love from / Samuel / Paris April 1956.*

63. *En attendant Godot.* Holograph manuscript signed, 151 pp. 4to, tipped to mounts, loose in sheets in half-morocco folding box.

64. *waiting for Godot. tragicomedy in 2 acts.* new york: grove press (1954). 8vo, original illustrated wrappers. First edition, inscribed in Beckett's hand:

> *This is the unexpurgated version of my translation of* En attendant Godot.

65. *Waiting for Godot.* Holograph manuscript signed, of Beckett's translation, 163 pp. In 2 small-4to notebooks, cloth-backed stiff wrappers, in half-morocco case.

66. *L'Innommable.* [Paris] Les Éditions de Minuit (1953). 12mo, original wrappers, uncut and unopened. First edition. Inscribed copy.

67. *L'Innommable.* Holograph manuscript signed, dated at beginning "29.3. 49" and at end "[?] janvier 1950." Written on verso of 156 folio pages, with additions on facing blanks. In 2 cloth-bound folio notebooks, the first inscribed by Beckett, "This is the original ms. of *L'Innommable* written 1949–50 and published by the Editions de Minuit 1953 . . ."

68. *The Unnamable. Translated from the French by the Author.* New York: Grove Press Inc. (1958). 8vo, original cloth-backed boards. One of 4 numbered copies, *hors commerce*, signed by Beckett.

69. *The Unnamable.* Holograph manuscript, 148 pp. In 3 notebooks, small 4to, cloth-backed wrappers, in half-morocco folding box. Titled and inscribed in Beckett's hand, "Original ms. of author's translation."

70. *The Unnamable.* Corrected typescript of Beckett's translation, 146 pp. 4to, half-morocco, raised bands, top edges gilt. Inscribed in his hand, "1st revision up to p. 25," and at end, "finished June 1958."

71. *Sur les monts les plus sauvages.* Autograph music manuscript signed, 2 pp. Folio. Draft, with revisions, of this aria from the opera *Benvenuto Cellini.* With the words.

Nearly one hundred years after the original publication, the memoirs of Benvenuto Cellini first appeared in French translation in 1822. Berlioz apparently read the book only a dozen years later, after his trip to Italy and, moved by Cellini's achievements against great odds, resolved to build an opera around his life. He began writing at the beginning of 1836 and finished in March 1837. The première took place on 10 September 1838.

In spite of the support of Théophile Gautier and a few other friends, *Benvenuto* was, officially, a failure. As with so many other of Berlioz's works, there was simply no audience. As one cynic put it at the time: "a miscarriage at the center of public indifference."

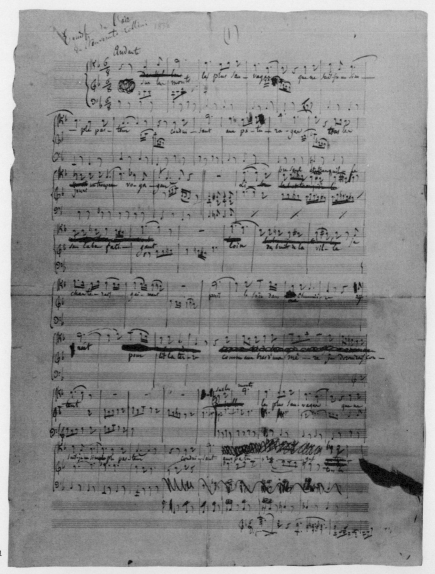

72. 6 original watercolors and 16 original ink drawings. 6½″ x 5⅛″. These unpublished watercolors and drawings were executed by Bonnard as covers of programs for musicales at the "Villa Bach." Five of the six watercolors are signed with Bonnard's monogram. All 22 compositions are drawn on heavy, handmade paper bearing the watermark "Dambricourt Frères, Halines, 1888," and all but one are formed of a sheet measuring 10¼″ x 6½″ folded in half, with Bonnard's drawing on the front cover. Seven of the pieces have, on the inside double-spread, a two-part musical program handwritten in ink and featuring piano duets by "Mr. et Mme. Terrasse"—Bonnard's sister Andrée and her husband, Claude Terrasse, composer of the music for Alfred Jarry's *Ubu roi* and *Par la taille* (see ALFRED JARRY, nos. 257, 259, 264, 265). Five of the six watercolors list the same program; two of the ink drawings list another. Two other drawings are accompanied by printed programs dated 3 February 1891 and 21 March 1891.

In the spring of 1891, Bonnard showed nine paintings at the Salon des Indépendants. In the course of a very favorable review of Bonnard's new work, the critic Gustave Geffroy commented on the influence of Gauguin and of Japanese woodcuts, a newly fashionable addiction of the French art world. These drawings also, naturally enough, reflect those two influences.

72

73. 5 holograph manuscript notebooks, totaling 425 pp. 4to and folio.

A few months before the Armistice of 1918, the poet Joë Bousquet, then 21, was seriously wounded, with permanent damage to his spinal cord. From then until his death in 1950, in spite of constant pain and confinement to his bed, he led a life that was uniquely active and influential. He wrote continuously, edited a little magazine—*Chantiers*—and formed friendships with many of the leading writers and artists of his time. They admired his work, made pilgrimages to his bedside in Carcassonne, and came, without exception, to consider their letters from and visits with him among their most enriching experiences. These friends included André Breton, Paul Éluard, Louis Aragon, Paul Valéry, Max Ernst, René Daumal, Jean Paulhan, Jean Dubuffet, Simone Weil, Hans Arp, Marcel Arland, René Char, Jean Cocteau, Albert Gleizes, Max Jacob, Marcel Jouhandeau, René Magritte, Joan Miró, and Yves Tanguy.

In these notebooks Bousquet sets down and analyzes his projects, tries them out in rough draft, criticizes them, sometimes drops them, but more often picks them up again another day from a different point of view, constantly reworking and reinventing them. There are drafts of stories and poems, philosophical and aesthetic observations, and notes on his reading—Rimbaud, Apollinaire, Gide, Éluard, Tzara, Roussel, and Nerval, for example—and on art—Klee, Ernst, Dali, Bellmer, and others.

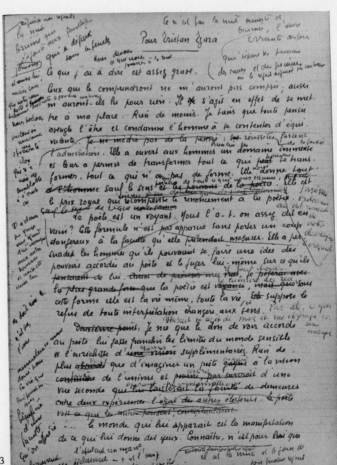

74. *La Connaissance du soir. Par Joë Bousquet.* [Paris] Les Éditions du Raisin [1945]. 4to, loose in sheets within original wrappers, uncut. In slipcase.

First edition of this collection of poems which Bousquet referred to as "pensefables" and "dansemuses." Printed in two colors by the Imprimerie Nationale in an edition limited to 200 numbered copies.

This copy, No. XXX, was printed for the book's publisher, Maurice Darantière, and bears his name. Laid in are holograph manuscripts signed (5 pp.) of two poems, *Lendemain* and *Madrigal.*

See also MARCEL JOUHANDEAU, no. 274, and JEAN PAULHAN, no. 344.

ANDRÉ BRETON

As the founder and forever leader (or "pope," as his detractors would have it) of the surrealist movement, Breton played a key role in the redirection of twentieth-century literary values.

Surrealism is founded on the belief in the higher reality of certain forms of association neglected until now, in the all-power of dream, in the undirected free play of thought. It tends to ruin definitively all other psychic mechanisms and to substitute itself for them in the resolution of the principal problems of life.

Manifeste du surréalisme, 1924

75. *13 études.* Holograph manuscript in Breton's hand, co-authored by Louis Aragon. With accompanying holograph letter signed. Published in *SIC*, 29 (May 1918).

76. *Façon.* Holograph manuscript signed. This poem, published first in *Les Trois Roses* (Grenoble), No. 3–4 (August–September 1918), was included in Breton's first book, *Mont de piété* (Paris: Au Sans Pareil, 1919).

77. *La Beauté sera convulsive ou ne sera pas.* Holograph manuscript signed, 3 pp. Folio, in grey Ingres folder marked in Breton's hand. A major text. Appeared first in *Minotaure,* 5 (12 May 1934), and then formed the first chapter of *L'Amour Fou* (Paris: Gallimard, 1937).

78. *Automatisme de la variante.* Holograph manuscript signed, 3 pp. Published in *Cahiers d'Art,* 5–6 (1935).

79. *Lumière Noire.* Holograph manuscript, 5 pp., very extensively corrected. Published first in *Le Monde Libre* (Montreal), I:2 (December 1943), then in *L'Arche* (Algiers), II:7 (December 1944–February 1945), and finally included in *Arcane 17, enté d'ajours* (Paris: Sagittaire, 1947).

Boys du siècle, interprètes anonymes, enchaînés et brillants de la revue à grand spectacle qui tend une vie sans espoir de changement, possède le théâtre mental...

[manuscrit autographe, texte raturé, en grande partie illisible]

77

LUMIÈRE NOIRE

toujours plus nombreux, plus perfectionnés,

Pardon de te marchander mon offrande, divinité insatiable de la guerre. Je sais tout ce qu'aujourd'hui on te donne et que tu n'as plus même à te baisser pour en prendre. Et si pourtant j'osais parler de ce qu'on te refuse! Une fois de plus tu es la hasard, fruit, à fracasser tes grands jouets bleus dans une nuit de mouches. Tu en profites pour faire dire qu'ayant toujours existé, tu existeras toujours. J'apporte que rien ne t'est si favorable que cette philosophie du retour éternel dont le dernier mot ne saurait être qu'à quoi bon...

[texte autographe, fortement raturé, en partie illisible]

79

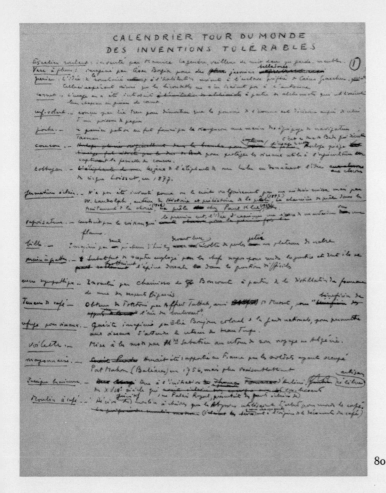

80

80. *Calendrier tour du monde des inventions tolérables.* Autograph manuscript signed, co-authored by Benjamin Péret, 5 pp. Text in the hand of Péret, signed by Breton. 4to, with corrections and deletions. A portion of this manuscript was published in *Almanach surréaliste du demi-siècle. Numéro spécial de La Nef*, 63–64 (March–April 1950).

81. *L'Un dans l'autre.* Holograph manuscript signed, 6 pp. 4to. Appeared in *Médium, nouvelle série*, 2 (February 1954). Collected in *L'Un dans l'autre* (Paris: Losfeld, 1970).

82. 2 holograph letters signed to Paul Éluard, 11 and 19 September 1932, 9 pp.

Intimate letters in which Breton, in the country with Valentine Hugo (then his mistress) and Max Ernst and his wife, tells of falling in love—"l'amour fou"— with a 25-year-old girl. After three days he proposes marriage.

en juillet 1932

Paul a envoyé Nush chez sa
mère pendant quelques
jours — un soir à Cyrano
.....
ensuite à la
foire de
Montmartre

85

83. 13 holograph letters and postcards, signed, to Victor Crastre, 1949–1959, 19 pp.

A warm, affectionate correspondence directed to a co-worker from the heroic period of the surrealist movement. Breton writes of Juan Gris (whom he thinks greatly overrated), Benjamin Péret, Apollinaire, Camus, Marcel Arland (of whom he disapproves), Julien Gracq, Aragon.

Crastre was one of a group of left-wing writers and political theorists behind the Marxist review *Clarté* with whom the surrealists were allied for a time in the mid-twenties in their attempt to find a common ground with Communism. They collaborated on the manifesto *La Révolution d'abord et toujours!*

84. *La Révolution d'abord et toujours!* Proof copy. Among those signing for *Clarté* (in addition to Crastre) were Jean Bernier and Marcel Fourrier; signing for the surrealists were Aragon, Artaud, Joë Bousquet, Breton, René Crevel, Robert Desnos, Éluard, Max Ernst, Michel Leiris, Benjamin Péret, and Philippe Soupault, among others.

85. Photographs of André Breton, some showing him with Valentine Hugo, Paul Éluard, Dali, and Gala.

86. *Mobile. Étude pour une représentation des États-Unis.* (Paris, 1962.) 4to, original wrappers, uncut.

First edition. One of 65 numbered copies on *vélin pur fil*. The title is, among other things, a reference to Calder's work. The book is dedicated to the memory of Jackson Pollock because, as Butor has explained, his first aerial view of the United States called to mind the image of Pollock at work on canvases laid flat on the studio floor.

87. *Mobile.* Typescript with some holograph corrections and additions, 274 pp., and holograph manuscript, 3 pp. Folio. Butor composes on the typewriter and this typescript and the one of *Litanie d'eau* were prepared by him.

88. *Illustrations.* [Paris] Gallimard (1964). 4to, original wrappers, uncut. First edition. Contains (principally) the long piece *Litanie d'eau.*

89. *Litanie d'eau.* Typescript, with some holograph markings, 61 pp., and holograph manuscript, 1 p. Folio. The typescript is marked in Butor's hand "version inédite." It is accompanied by a holograph letter signed, 29 May 1967, transmitting the script to Yves Gandon, of the Maison Internationale des Pen-Clubs, Paris.

90. *La Dévotion à la croix. Pièce en trois journées. Texte français d'Albert Camus* by Pedro Calderón de la Barca. [Paris, 1953]. 12mo, original wrappers, uncut and unopened. First edition of Camus's version, prepared for the Festival of Angers in 1953. One of 65 numbered copies on *vélin pur fil.*

91. *La Dévotion à la croix. Pièce en trois journées.* [Paris, 1953]. Another copy, this one on *papier alfama,* inscribed:

A *Jacques Hébertot, / avec l'amical hommage / d'Albert Camus.*

Jacques Hébertot was the original producer of Camus's plays *Caligula* and *Les Justes.*

92. *La Dévotion à la croix.* Manuscript signed and dated 1953, composed of 77 sheets, some holograph, some typescript. The typescript is almost completely rewritten throughout.

93. *Discours de Suède.* Paris: Gallimard (1958). 12mo, original wrappers, uncut.

First edition. One of 56 copies on *Hollande van Gelder.* Camus's speech of acceptance at the Nobel Prize ceremony, 10 December 1957, and his lecture entitled *L'Artiste et son temps* given at the University of Upsala four days later.

94. *Discours de Suède.* The maquette for the published volume, including corrected typescripts of both lectures, with holograph additions, 40 pp.

95. *Chamfort.* Holograph manuscript, 6 pp. Small 4to. For Camus, Chamfort was one of the most passionate of French moralists, closer to such novelists as Stendhal, Mme. de La Fayette, and Benjamin Constant than to other aphorists, such as La Rochefoucauld or Vauvenargues.

LOUIS-FERDINAND CÉLINE

96. *Guignol's Band. Roman.* Paris: Les Éditions Denoël (1944). 8vo, original wrappers, uncut. First edition. With the Sisley Huddleston bookplate.

97. *Guignol's Band. Roman.* Paris: Gallimard (1952). 8vo, original wrappers, uncut. Second edition.

98. *Le Pont de Londres. Guignol's Band II.* [Paris] Gallimard (1964). 8vo, original wrappers, uncut. First edition.

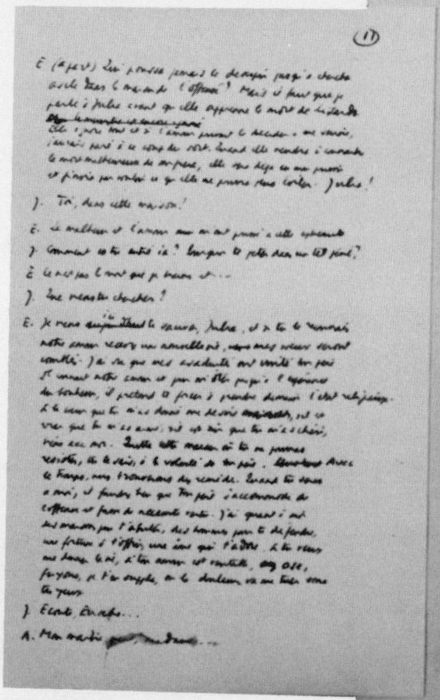

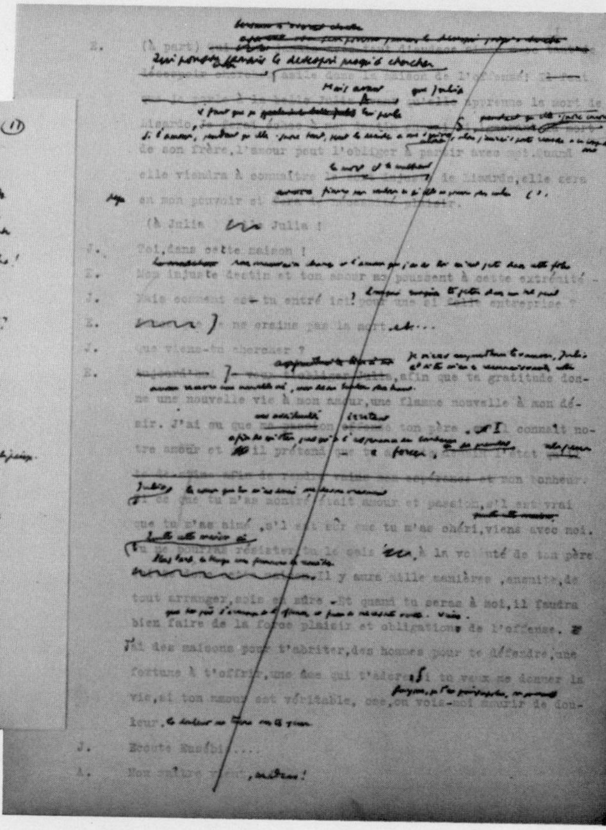

E. (à part) ... asile dans la maison de l'offensé! ...

... apprenne la mort de Risardo, ...

de son frère, l'amour peut l'obliger à partir avec moi. Quand

elle viendra à connaître ... de Risardo, elle sera

en mon pouvoir si ...

(à Julia ...) ... Julia !

J. Toi, dans cette maison !

E. Mon injuste destin et ton amour me poussent à cette extrémité.

J. Mais comment es-tu entré ici pour une si ... entreprise ?

E. ... ne crains pas la mort ...

J. Que viens-tu chercher ?

E. ... afin que ta gratitude donne une nouvelle vie à mon amour, une flamme nouvelle à mon désir. J'ai su que ... ton père ... il connaît notre amour et il prétend que ... mon bonheur.

... ce que tu m'as montré était amour et passion, s'il est vrai que tu m'as aimé, s'il est sûr que tu m'as chéri, viens avec moi. ... à la volonté de ton père ... Il y aura mille manières, ensuite, de tout arranger, sois en sûre. Et quand tu seras à moi, il faudra bien faire de la force plaisir et obligations de l'offense.

J'ai des maisons pour t'abriter, des hommes pour te défendre, une fortune à t'offrir, une âme qui t'adore ... si tu veux me donner la vie, si ton amour est véritable, ... ou vois-moi mourir de douleur.

J. Ecoute Eusébio....

A. Mon maître ..., madame!

92

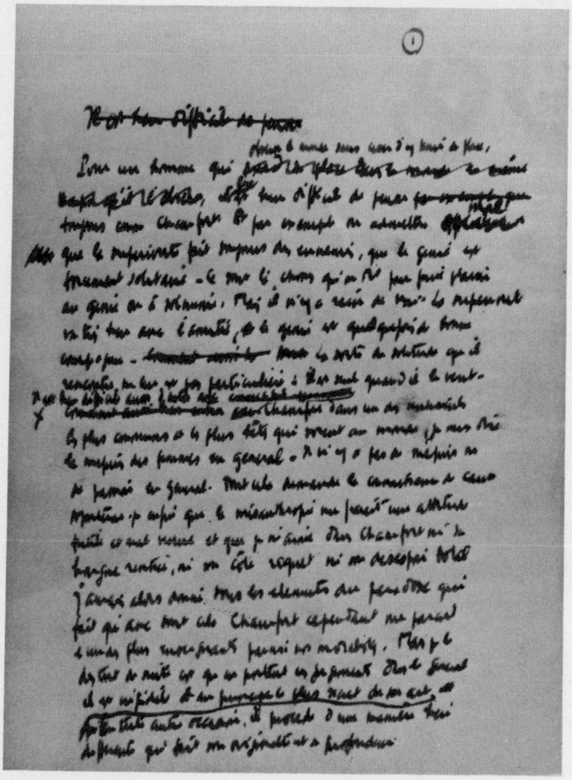

95

99. *Guignol's Band* [and its sequel, *Le Pont de Londres*]. The complete manuscript of the 2 volumes, in combinations of holograph manuscript, typescript, and corrected typescript with holograph additions, totaling 4,022 pp. 4to and folio.

Guignol's Band and its sequel, *Le Pont de Londres*, were written as one novel, but it was so long that Robert Denoël published only the first half in his edition of 1944. Soon after the Liberation, while enemies at both ends of the political spectrum were howling for Céline's blood, his apartment was ransacked and his papers disappeared, including a number of manuscripts. Among them was the second part of *Guignol's Band*. In 1962, a year after Céline's death, his former secretary, in cleaning out a closet, came across a bundle of typescript from which that second part could be published.

Guignol's Band, in its current edition, is made up of 17 unnumbered chapters totaling 314 pages. *Le Pont de Londres* is divided into 24 unnumbered chapters, running to 406 pages. The present manuscript is that of the two volumes, totals 4,022 pages, and includes five different versions of *Guignol's Band*. The various scripts for *Le Pont de Londres* show three differing versions. Corrections are in ink and in Céline's hand throughout. Céline was a tireless, almost obsessive, rewriter. This unique manuscript group gives an incomparable insight into that characteristic process.

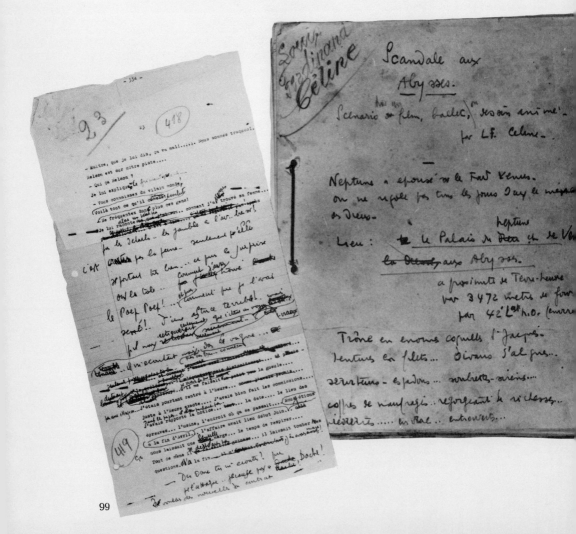

100. *Ballets sans musique, sans personne, sans rien. Illustrations d'Éliane Bonabel.* [Paris] Gallimard (1959). 8vo, original wrappers, uncut and unopened.

101. *Scandale aux abysses.* Holograph manuscript signed, 118 pp., of which 60 have earlier draft versions on verso. Folio. The complete manuscript of Céline's principal ballet (included in the preceding volume).

102. *Scandale aux abysses.* Proofs of the first half of the text of an edition designed and set up by Jean-Gabriel Daragnès but never published. With some corrections, 20 pp. 4to.

103. 59 holograph letters signed by Céline to his friend Mourlet, in Quimper, 1941–1950, 116 sides. 8vo, 4to, and folio. Signed "LF," "LD," "Dest.," and "Destouches" (Céline's real name); a few toward the end are also signed by Céline's wife, Lucette.

Witty, bitter, vitriolic, scatological, these letters cover the war years and Céline's exile in Denmark. Written from Bezons, Paris, Copenhagen, and Korsor.

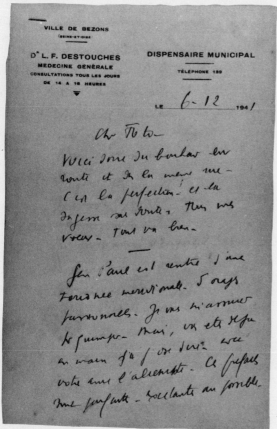

103

104. *Le Plan de l'aiguille.* Paris: Au Sans Pareil, 1929. 8vo, original wrappers, uncut. First edition. Review copy, inscribed to the critic Émile Vuillermoz:

à Vuillermoz / hommage de Blaise Cendrars.

This novel, twelve years in the writing, has for its central character Dan Yack, a restless adventurer who is the projection of Cendrars himself. In a later work (*Bourlinguer*, 1948), Cendrars wrote, "My ambition is not to write, but to live . . . . I want to find out who I am . . . ."

105. *Le Plan de l'aiguille.* The complete manuscript, made up of corrected typescript with holograph additions, 379 pp. Folio.

PAUL CÉZANNE

106. 6 holograph letters signed to his son, Paul, August–October 1906, 25½ pp. 8vo, with envelopes.

These six letters written by Cézanne from Aix to his son in Paris during the last weeks of his life are among the most important known. Barely two hundred letters of Cézanne have been traced and not all of them have survived. About half are the boyhood letters he wrote to Émile Zola, which were bequeathed by Mme. Zola to the Bibliothèque Nationale. These six give a very moving picture of Cézanne at the end of his life: his temperament, his health, the conditions under which he worked, and his total absorption in his work. He gets up very early in order to be at work before five because by eight the heat becomes unbearable. It slows down considerably the workings of his brain so that he finds it impossible any longer to "think in painting."

> I can tell you that as a painter I am growing more lucid before nature, but . . . the expression of my sensations keeps growing more difficult. I can't achieve the intensity that builds up in my senses. I don't have that magnificent richness of color that animates nature . . . . Here by the riverbank, motifs keep multiplying; the same subject seen from a different angle offers another subject of the greatest interest and so varied that I think I could keep busy for months at a time without moving from that spot, just by bending a bit to the right or to the left . . . .

Diabetic and weakening, Cézanne still insists on painting outdoors. He has to be driven to the river (the Arc) to work. But in spite of physical weakness his spirit remains eager: he is still searching. The only thing that keeps him indoors is rain. He has moved from the riverbank to the Beauregard quarter, where the road begins to climb—very picturesque but exposed to the mistral. He has climbed the route on foot with only a watercolor kit because that is easier to carry. He feels his nervous system is very much weaker. The only thing that keeps him going is his painting. ". . . I must keep on. I must be able to paint what I see, based on nature . . . ."

16

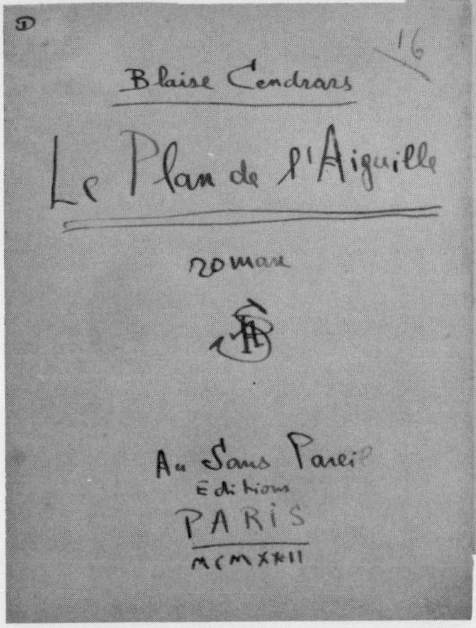

Blaise Cendrars

Le Plan de l'Aiguille

roman

Au Sans Pareil
Editions
PARIS
MCMXXII

2 17

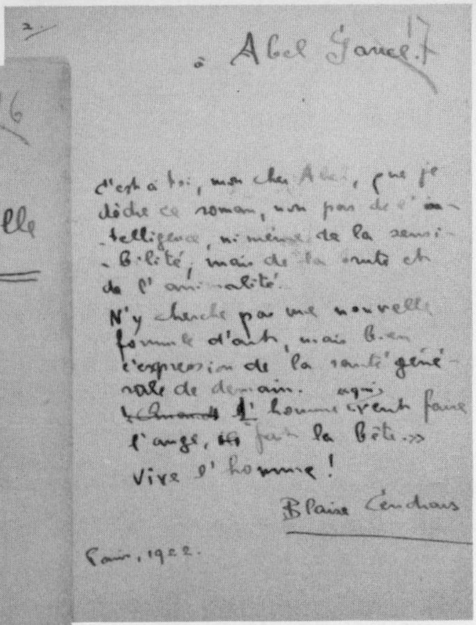

à Abel Gance.

C'est à toi, mon cher Abel, que je dédie ce roman, non pas de l'intelligence, ni même de la sensibilité, mais de la santé et de l'animalité.
N'y cherche pas une nouvelle formule d'art, mais bien l'expression de la santé générale de demain. « qui l'homme veut faire l'ange, et fait la bête. »
Vive l'homme !

Blaise Cendrars

Paris, 1922.

105

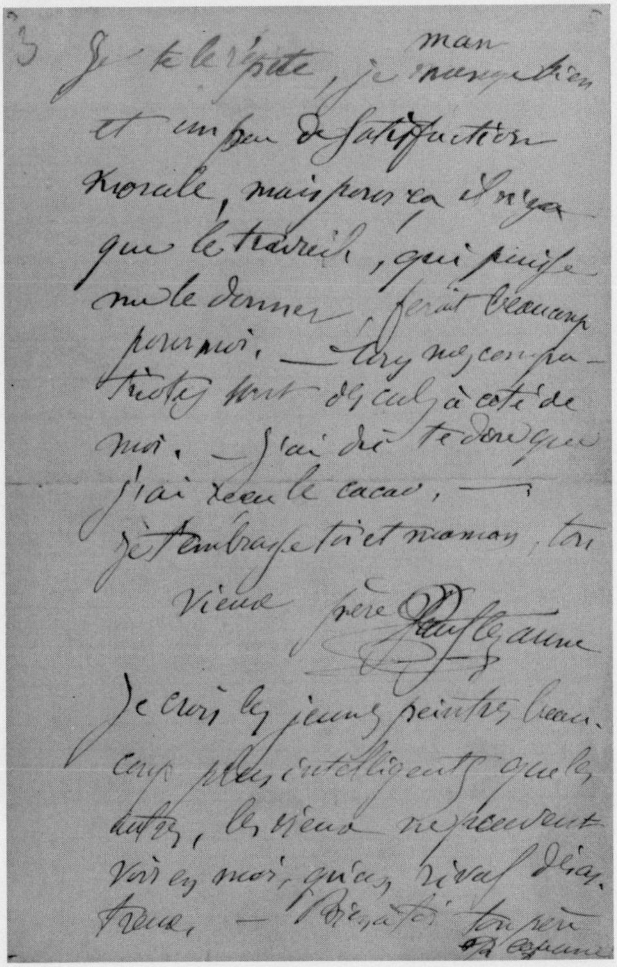

3 Je te le répète, je mange bien et un peu de satisfaction morale, mais pour ça il n'y a que le travail, qui puisse me le donner, serait beaucoup pour moi. — Tous mes compatriotes sont des culs à côté de moi. — J'ai dû te dire que j'ai reçu le cacao. —
Je t'embrasse toi et maman, ton vieux père Paul Cézanne

Je crois les jeunes peintres beaucoup plus intelligents que les autres, les vieux ne peuvent voir en moi qu'un rival désastreux. — Bien à toi toujours
P. Cézanne

106

107

Monsieur Cézanne artiste Peintre
Paris, le   18

10	Blanc d'argent		10
10	vert véronèse a		
	Ocre jaune a		
1/4	laque fine a		
3	vermillon		
1	vert émeraude		
10	jaune brillant		
		Total 66	25

Mon cher Monsieur Cézanne
je vous remercie bien de vos bons
souvenirs à notre égard
Nous vous soutenons bien le bonjour
à vous et à toute votre famille

109

In his last letter, written only a few hours before going out to paint for the last time, he writes:

> . . . I keep on working, with difficulty, but in the end there is something. That is the important thing . . . . Since what I do is based on sensations, I think it is impossible to explain it. I am well enough . . . but to give you the kind of news you'd like to have, I would have to be twenty years younger . . . . A little moral satisfaction would do a lot for me but only my work can give me that . . . .

107. *Tête de Paul*. Pencil drawing by Cézanne of his son as a young boy. 5½" x 4½".

108. Facsimile of the notebook found in Cézanne's pocket after his death. 4 1-2" x 2 13-16". In board slipcase.

On 15 October 1906, Cézanne was out painting, as usual. It was raining and he caught a chill and collapsed on the way home. He was picked up by a passing laundry cart driver. The day after that he was out again around six, working on a portrait of Vallier. He came home in a state of collapse and was put to bed. Pneumonia set in. From time to time he would get up to add a touch to an unfinished watercolor. On the 22nd he died. In his jacket pocket was a small notebook in which he had been making his last sketches, notes, jogs to memory about paints and medicines he needed. This facsimile is one of a small number of copies made by Daniel Jacomet for the Cézanne family.

109. Accounts, receipted bills, and postal-money-order stubs relating to Cézanne's purchases of painting materials from Julien Tanguy ("le père Tanguy"), celebrated Montmartre painting-supplies dealer who was first the supplier and friend, then backer, collector, and dealer of many of the Impressionist and post-Impressionist painters (Cézanne, van Gogh, Seurat, Gauguin, Monet, and Sisley, among others); covering the period 1873–1890, a total of 17 sheets, various sizes, some recto-verso. Two of the documents bear letters from Tanguy to Cézanne, and six have annotations in Cézanne's hand.

One long recapitulation shows in detail Cézanne's purchases of painting materials between May 1873 and February 1885. Tanguy was reputed to put high prices on his favorite paintings in order not to have to part with them. This habit, combined with the chronic delinquency of his accounts receivable, made him, in turn, slow pay. In 1885 his landlord was trying to evict him—thus his gentle request for Cézanne's attention to a bill representing twelve years' supplies.

Until 1893, Tanguy's shop was the only place in Paris where Cézanne's canvases could be seen. It was there that Ambroise Vollard purchased his first Cézannes, which he showed in his historic Cézanne exhibition of 1895.

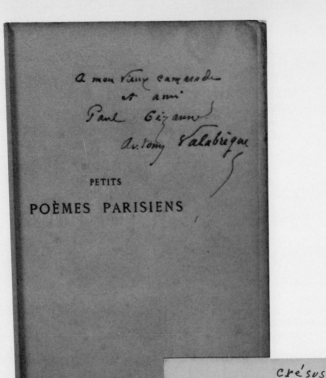

PETITS

POÈMES PARISIENS

110

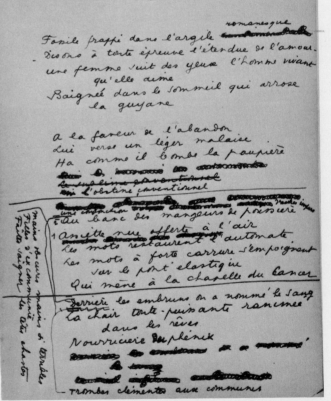

113

110. Three books from Cézanne's library, with presentation inscriptions to him from their authors:

L'Age d'or by Marc Lafargue. Paris, 1903. Inscribed:

> *à Paul Cézanne / hommage de ma / respectueuse admiration. / Marc Lafargue.*

Essai sur le naturisme by Maurice Le Blond. Paris, 1896. Inscribed:

> *à M. Paul Cézanne / hommage respectueux / Maurice Le Blond / Juin 98.*

Petits poèmes parisiens by Antony Valabrègue. Paris, 1880. Inscribed:

> *A mon vieux camarade / et ami / Paul Cézanne / Antony Valabrègue.*

Valabrègue, poet and art critic, met Cézanne in 1860. Cézanne painted his portrait three times (Venturi 126, 127, 128) and included him in two group studies (Venturi 96, 120). He often referred to him as "le grand Valabrègue."

111. *Portrait de Cézanne.* Original lithograph. This self-portrait was executed for the third (unpublished) *Album des Peintres-Graveurs*, 1898. Proof on *Ingres d'Arches.* (Venturi 1,158; Johnson 31.)

112. *L'Oeuvre* by Émile Zola. Paris: Charpentier, 1886. 12mo, full black morocco, raised bands, decorative pattern formed of blind-stamping and gilt fillets, inner gilt dentelles, all edges gilt, original wrappers bound in, within slipcase (binding by Semet & Plumelle). First edition. One of 175 numbered copies on *papier de Hollande.*

This book's publication ended the friendship between Cézanne and Zola: Cézanne saw himself in Zola's portrayal of Claude Lantier, and thought the interpretation of his art a harsh one.

RENÉ CHAR

Char, as much as anyone, is the poet of our times, the strong voice and the conscience of an anguished, fragmenting world.

> Nous touchons au temps du suprême désespoir et de l'espoir pour rien, au temps indescriptible . . . c'est pourquoi il est grand temps de nous composer une santé du malheur. Dût-elle avoir l'apparence de l'arrogance du miracle.
>
> *A une sérénité crispée,* 1951

113. *Crésus.* Holograph manuscript, 1½ pp. 4to, with envelope addressed to Valentine Hugo.

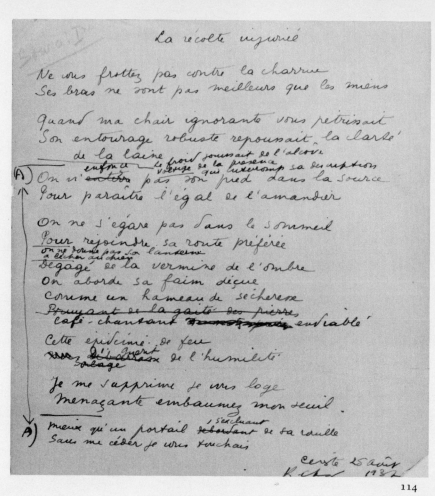

114.

114. *La Récolte injuriée.* Holograph manuscript signed, 1937, 3 pp. Early draft, together with finished version.

115. *Rêve du 22 mars 1938—6 heures du matin.* Holograph manuscript signed, 2½ pp. 4to. Originally titled *Épuration d'une aube.*

116. *Le Rempart de brindilles.* Manuscript, part holograph, part corrected typescript [1953], 5 pp. Folio, morocco-backed boards, bound with corrected proofs of *Les Transparents* (*Les Matinaux*, revised version, 1954), 4 pp.

117. *Victoire éclair.* Holograph manuscript signed, 16 May 1954. Revised version of a poem entitled in its earlier form *Calendrier éclair.*

118. *Dansez, montagnes.* Holograph manuscript signed, 12 April 1961. A prose poem, honoring Miró.

119. *Monôme*. Holograph manuscript signed.

120. *La Truite*. Holograph manuscript signed.

121. *La Boucle retrouvée* by Guillaume Apollinaire. Autograph manuscript copy in Char's hand of one of his favorite poems from *Calligrammes*.

122. *Hiéroglyphe* by Charles Cros. Autograph manuscript copy in Char's hand of a poem he particularly liked in *Le Collier de griffes* (1908).

123. Holograph letters signed, addressed to Valentine Hugo, together with related documents, 1933–1967, 52 pieces.

> Valentine Hugo was an intimate friend of most of the leading surrealists and was herself a member of the group. Over the years, she made many portraits, in all media, of the principal writers, artists, and musicians, within the group and outside it.

124. *Portrait de René Char* by Valentine Hugo. Pencil. Measures 12⅛″ x 7⅞″.

125. Char's astrological chart, prepared by Valentine Hugo.

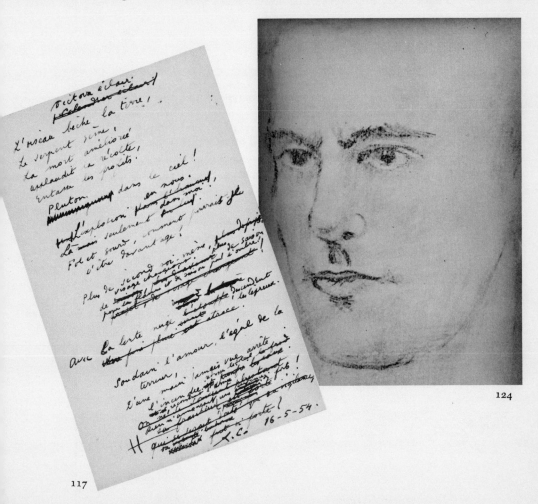

124

126. *Le Roi Arthus.* Holograph music manuscript signed, 1892–1895. Opera in three acts, written on 194 sheets, with additions and variants on verso of 123 of these. Folio, with a holograph presentation inscription to Gustave Samazeuilh.

Chausson came to music late, entering the Conservatoire at the age of twenty-five after giving up the study of law. He left the Conservatoire to study privately with César Franck. His first works were published in 1878, but it was only in 1891, with the première of his Symphony in B-Flat Major, that the importance of his gifts was recognized. He was at the height of his creative powers and on the eve of winning a wider acceptance, when he died in 1899 after a bicycle accident.

PAUL CLAUDEL

127. *Cinq grandes odes suivies d'un processionnal pour saluer le siècle nouveau.* Paris: L'Occident, 1910. Folio, three-quarter maroon morocco, raised bands, top edges gilt, original wrappers bound in (binding by Alix). First edition, limited to 215 numbered copies.

One of the essential works of Claudel. In a letter to his friend Gabriel Frizeau dated 1 May 1908, Claudel wrote:

I have finished my *Cinq odes suivies d'un processionnal* and I shall publish them, no doubt, next year in as handsome an edition as possible . . . . They all bear on the same theme: the rapture of the poet in full possession of his powers of expression, mingling with the memories of his past life, in the ecstacy of liberty finally achieved, the contemplation of a *universe* now *Catholic.* It will be the pause and the bell that will announce the second part of my works (if it comes).

Claudel had been a passive Christian, approaching religion as a literary man through Pascal, Newman, and others, and sensitive mostly to the aesthetic aspects of the ritual. But on Christmas Day 1886, in Notre-Dame cathedral, God revealed Himself to him. And, as he later wrote, "In an instant my heart was touched and I believed." From then on, the Church and its dogma were the rock on which he built his work.

Claudel wrote in 1913 that his reading of Rimbaud just prior to the Notre Dame experience "opened a fissure in my materialist prison and gave me the living, almost physical, impression of the supernatural."

As a student, Saint-John Perse (Alexis Saint-Léger Léger) met Paul Claudel through Francis Jammes, and the effect on him of Claudel's *Cinq grandes odes* is evident, particularly in *Anabase* (Paris, 1924).

Claudel's incantatory powers made a great impression on many younger poets, including a number (Paul Éluard, for example) who had little use for Claudel the man or his religious beliefs.

128. *Cinq grandes odes* . . . . Holograph manuscript, 1906–1907, 88 pp. Folio.

The original manuscript of the first ode, *Les Muses*, published separately in 1905 by the Bibliothèque de l'Occident, has never been found. In 1910 the same publisher brought out the complete work. The present manuscript, from which the book was printed, is complete—except for the lost first part.

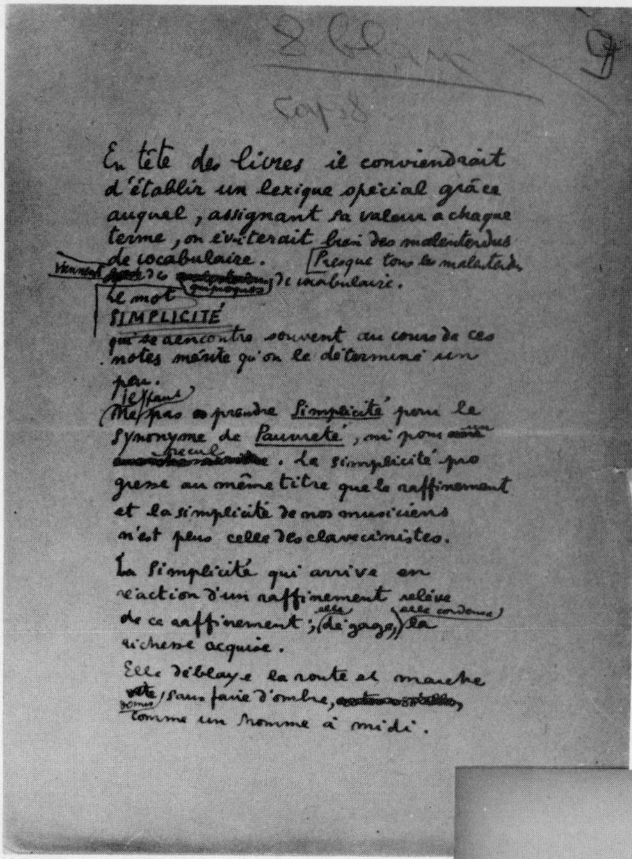

En tête des livres il conviendrait
d'établir un lexique spécial grâce
auquel, assignant sa valeur à chaque
terme, on éviterait bien des malentendus
de vocabulaire.   [Presque tous les malentendus
sont de vocabulaire.]

Le mot
SIMPLICITÉ
qui se rencontre souvent au cours de ces
notes mérite qu'on le détermine un
peu.

Ne pas prendre simplicité pour le
synonyme de pauvreté, ni pour
recul . La simplicité pro
gresse au même titre que le raffinement
et la simplicité de nos musiciens
n'est plus celle des clavecinistes.

La simplicité qui arrive en
réaction d'un raffinement relève
de ce raffinement ; (dégage) la
richesse acquise.

Elle déblaye la route et marche
sans faire d'ombre,
comme un homme à midi.

130

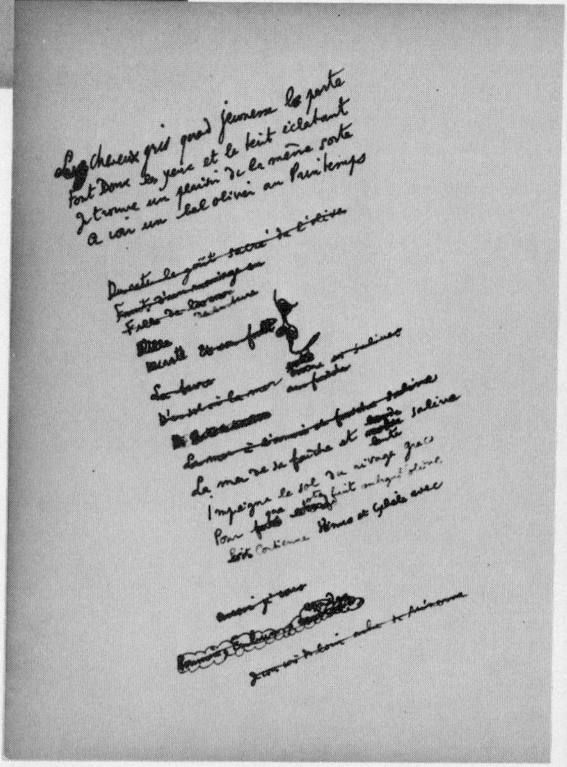

132

129. *Le Coq et l'arlequin.—Notes autour de la musique. Avec un Portrait de l'auteur et Deux Monogrammes par P. Picasso.* Paris: Éditions de la Sirène, 1918. 16mo, original wrappers, uncut. First edition.

The Éditions de la Sirène had recently been founded by Cocteau and Blaise Cendrars. Through this witty, aphoristic little book on music, Cocteau managed to focus a good deal of attention on the new publishing venture—and on himself. He had only kind things to say about Satie, was somewhat less generous toward Stravinsky, and was rather harsh about Debussy. He wanted to turn the attention of the young away from the Debussy heritage to the new—a combination of Satie, the American jazz-band and music-hall influence, and *Les Six* (Georges Auric—to whom the book is dedicated—Darius Milhaud, Francis Poulenc, Arthur Honegger, Germaine Tailleferre, and Louis Durey). The book evoked a good deal of outraged disparagement and a somewhat condescending, ungenerous review from Gide, in the form of an "open letter" in the *Nouvelle Revue Française* for June 1919.

130. *Le Coq et l'arlequin.* Maquette for the original edition, consisting of the complete manuscript, part holograph and part typescript with holograph corrections in ink by Cocteau. The text was cut out and tipped onto folio sheets of light cardboard and prepared for the printer, with instructions in blue crayon, by Blaise Cendrars. (Cendrars's difficult scrawl was the result of a late conversion to left-handedness after the loss of his right arm.)

131. *Vocabulaire. Poèmes.* Paris: Éditions de la Sirène, 1922. 12mo, original wrappers, uncut. First edition. One of 1,100 numbered copies on *papier alfa vélin d'Ecosse.* Daragnès bookplate.

132. *Vocabulaire.* Holograph manuscripts of 20 poems from the book, some in two and three versions, and many differing substantially from the printed texts.

The manuscript for the poem *Les Yeux doux* is of special interest: on nine separate sheets Cocteau has set down ideas, rhymes, and early drafts for the poem, enabling us to follow its evolution from the beginning to a tentatively complete version which, under the title *Gloires,* and with an additional (and somewhat redundant) line, inverts the order of its eventual, finished form.

The linen-bound "Sketcher's Note Book" contains, among other poems, sketches, and notes, an early, heavily corrected draft of the poem *Les Cheveux gris, quand jeunesse les porte.*

133. *Le Grand écart. Roman.* Paris: Librairie Stock, 1923. 8vo, original wrappers, uncut. First edition (marked, for publicity purposes, "Deuxième édition"). Presentation copy, inscribed:

> *Mon cher / Daragnès / considérez cet / envoi comme / un / souvenir très / amical / Jean Cocteau / Mai 1923.* [Colophon date is 25 April 1923.]

A delightful novel based on reminiscences of his late teens by the post-thirty Cocteau. It is a period piece: as he wrote to his mother, "A *Confession d'un enfant du siècle* in very simple and lively form."

134. *Le Grand écart*. Page proofs corrected by Cocteau. 8vo, three-quarter crushed levant, raised bands, top edges gilt, other edges untrimmed. Tipped in is the label, in Cocteau's hand, used for returning the proofs to the Imprimerie Darantière in Dijon.

135. *Le Livre blanc*. (Paris: Maurice Sachs et Jacques Bonjean) 1928. Small 4to, full beige calf, original wrappers bound in, uncut.

> First edition of Cocteau's rarest book, an autobiographical memoir in the form of a novel. It was published anonymously and limited to 21 copies for sale and 10 author's copies, all on *papier vergé blanc de Montval*, handmade by Gaspard Maillol.
>> This copy is one of the 10 author's copies (No. IX). Bound in with it are page proofs on heavy vellum, corrected in ink by Cocteau.

136. *Le Livre blanc*. Typescript with holograph corrections in ink dated "Chablis Décembre 1927," 44 pp. 4to. It was from this typescript that the book was printed.

137. *Le Livre blanc*. Another copy of the typescript, with manuscript introduction in the hand of the writer Jean Desbordes, Cocteau's secretary and protégé.

138. *Le Livre blanc*. Page proofs in (trial?) 8vo format, corrected throughout by Cocteau.

139. *Les Parents terribles*. Holograph manuscript, 54 pp. Folio. First draft of the play. Marked in Cocteau's hand, "Reread, very important . . . perhaps add to First Act some passages of [this newly] rediscovered first draft."

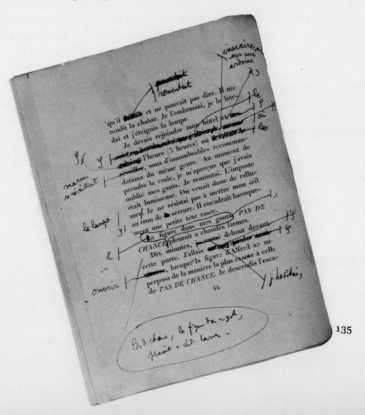

140. *Les Parents terribles*. 3 pastel drawings by Cocteau for an illustrated edition of the play. 10 9-16″ x 8 1-4″ (2) and 8 1-4″ x 10 5-8″. Together with holograph note [to J. Festy, Gallimard production chief], 21 April 1956, concerning that edition.

141. 6 holograph letters signed to Walter Berry, American lawyer in Paris and companion of Edith Wharton, 1918–1924.

> . . . The only one to blame is Proust. He *knew* that his coming after 9:30—ten minutes to ten—[to a private reading of Cocteau's work] would upset me. He has forgotten that I too am a *sick man* and a poet . . . I have read the three [volumes of Proust]. He is managing to bring off a great work by being concerned only with the confusions of social rank and by ransacking [real] people instead of developing characters. Just so long as one finds again, at the end, the rich material of Swann's jealousy. If not, there would be a sort of disequilibrium.

> The final letter concerns and exhibits his own disequilibrium after the death of Raymond Radiguet.

142. Holograph letter signed to Valentine Hugo, 4 September 1922. Includes a drawing of Stravinsky in Nijinsky's dressing room, ". . . une scène de souvenirs des Ballets Russes—Bonne Époque . . . ."

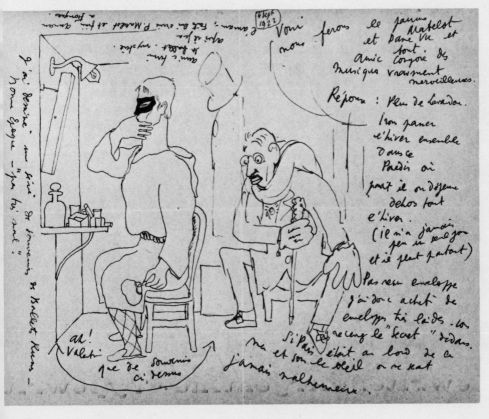

143. 12 holograph letters signed to Pierre Herbart, 1928–1930. Cocteau's struggles with opium addiction, reminiscences of Radiguet and Raymond Roussel, gossip of Gide and Auric, and his concern over his protégé Jean Desbordes, whom he had "entrusted" to Herbart.

144. 2 holograph letters signed to Jean Desbordes, May 1929. Cocteau writes, as an anguished mother hen, to his absent son-substitute, before and after receiving a letter from him.

145. *Portrait de Valentine Hugo.* Pen-and-ink. 10½″ x 8⅛″. Valentine Hugo was a close friend of Cocteau's. Originally, Cocteau's mother had hoped Valentine might become her daughter-in-law. As Valentine became more involved with the surrealists, she saw less of Cocteau.

146. *J'Adore.* [*Préface de Jean Cocteau*] by Jean Desbordes. Paris: Bernard Grasset, 1928. 12mo, original wrappers, uncut and unopened. First edition, marked 5th edition on the cover for publicity purposes. Presentation copy inscribed:

> *A Monsieur Émile Vuillermoz / timidement / avec le / secret espoir de lui plaire / Jean Desbordes.*

Cocteau had hoped that his new protégé would achieve the literary celebrity of his earlier one, Raymond Radiguet. In the original prospectus, laid in and illustrated with a picture of Desbordes in his Navy uniform, that hope appears in a paragraph beginning, "Jean Desbordes arrives as the answer to a universal demand . . . ." The critics thought otherwise.

COLETTE

147. *Chéri. Roman* by Colette Willy. Paris: Arthème Fayard et Cie., 1920. 8vo, original wrappers, uncut. First edition. With the collaboration of Léopold Marchand, a more experienced writer for the theatre, Colette made a play of *Chéri*, which opened at the Théâtre Michel on 31 December 1921.

148. *Chéri.* Holograph manuscript and corrected typescript of the first two acts, with many variants from the final version, 183 pp. Folio.

149. *La Seconde. Roman.* Paris: Ferenczi (1929). 8vo, original wrappers, uncut.

First edition. One of 200 author's copies on *papier simili-Japon* of various colors, this one on Colette's favorite shade of blue. Inscribed:

> *A Daragnès / ce "rappel de bleu" / —à cause de ses / yeux naturellement! / Sa vieille amie / Colette*

With the Daragnès bookplate. (Jean-Gabriel Daragnès, painter, engraver, book-designer, and printer, brought out limited editions of several books by Colette on his hand press.)

Colette eventually made a play out of this novel, too—again with the collaboration of Léopold Marchand. It had its première at the Théâtre de la Madeleine on 23 January 1951.

150. *La Seconde*. Holograph manuscript and corrected typescript, 346 pp. Folio, in first- and early-draft form. Some scenes are present in several states and show substantial variants from the published version. The entire first act (of the four in this script) was omitted from the published version.

151. *J'ai connu à Daragnès* .... Holograph manuscript, 3 pp. 4to. Accompanied by a corrected typescript of the same text. An impressionistically colorful portrait of an old friend.

152. 34 holograph letters signed to Émile Vuillermoz, 1907–1933.

The correspondence takes its source in the early professional association of Colette and "Vuill," in the first decade of the century. She was then a dancer and music-hall artiste, whose eminence as France's leading woman writer was as yet perceptible only to her husband, Henri Gauthier-Villars (Willy), who cheerfully exploited her literary talent under his own name. Vuillermoz, pupil of Gabriel Fauré, friend and early supporter of Debussy and Ravel, was still a long way from his eventual role as France's most prominent music critic. On commission from Willy-as-impresario, he was writing the music for Colette's music-hall turns. She recalls that period affectionately in a 3-page typed memoir included with the correspondence.

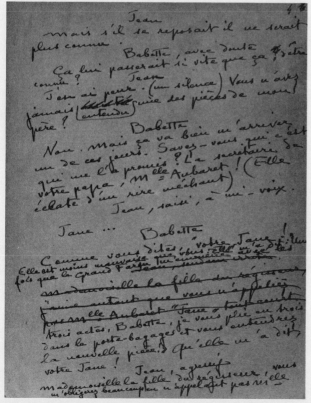

154

155

153. 4 holograph letters and 1 postcard, signed, from Olympe Terrain to un-identified correspondents, 22 pp. Written by Colette's school principal in her hometown of St.-Sauveur-en-Puisaye, this correspondence gives firsthand details concerning Colette's childhood, adolescence, school career, and early writings, including a heavy dose of family scandal. (Mme. Terrain had been deeply hurt by Colette's treatment of her in the *Claudine* series.)

154. Photographs of Colette, showing her across the years as dancer, actress, writer. Some inscribed.

CLAUDE DEBUSSY

155. *En Sourdine.* Holograph music manuscript signed, 5 pp.

In 1871, when he was nine, Debussy began to study piano with Mme. Mauté de Fleurville. She had been a pupil of Chopin's, and her daughter Mathilde had married Paul Verlaine only the year before.

In 1882 Debussy composed settings for three of Verlaine's *Fêtes Galantes*, including *En Sourdine*, and gave the present manuscript to Catherine Stevens, daughter of the Belgian painter Alfred Stevens. Catherine was already engaged to be married, but Debussy had dreams of making her change her mind. Years later she told René Peter that Debussy had asked her whether she felt her father would give him permission to marry her, after *Pelléas et Mélisande* was produced and he was rich. "Take care of *Pelléas* first," she told him. "We'll talk about the rest then." But by the time *Pelléas* was finally produced, they both had long since made other arrangements.

The first page of this manuscript carries the title in red ink and in Debussy's hand. On the second page is the following presentation inscription:

> *à Mademoiselle Catherine Stevens / en hommage / et pour marquer un peu de ma joie / d'être son affectueusement dévoué. / C. Debussy.*

156. *La damoiselle élue. Poème lyrique d'après D. G. Rossetti. Traduction française de Gabriel Sarrazin. Partition chant et piano, réduite par l'auteur.* Paris: Librairie de l'Art Indépendant, 1893. Folio, full vellum, top edges gilt, original wrappers bound in, uncut.

First printing. One of 4 numbered copies on China paper of a total edition of 160. The cover, an original lithograph in color by Maurice Denis, is one of the painter's earliest works. With the following presentation inscription:

> *avec toute ma sympathie pour / Pierre Louÿs / Claude Debussy / Juillet 93.*

La damoiselle élue was written by Debussy in 1887 but not performed publicly until 1893. Debussy and Pierre Louÿs had met in March 1893, at the Cabaret du Clou in the Avenue Trudaine in Paris, a gathering place for artists, where Erik Satie was house pianist. Louÿs told Debussy of his interest in Debussy's second work, *Cinq poèmes de Baudelaire* (1890). Their friendship deepened and in 1897 Debussy set to music some of Pierre Louÿs's *Chansons de Bilitis*.

La damoiselle élue

*Serai les champs d'airy
portant la fleur d'absinthe
je suis la femme peinte
par Maurice Denis.*

(P. L.)

chez Bailly, éditeur rue de la Chaussée d'Antin

157

IL A ÉTÉ TIRÉ

cinquante exemplaires numérotés sur papier Japon

cinquante exemplaires numérotés sur papier de Hollande.

à Monsieur A. Carré.
et plus encore à l'artiste qui sut créer
l'atmosphère de rêve inoubliable sans laquelle
Pelléas et Mélisande n'auraient pas vivre.

Claude Debussy

Mai / 1902.

159

157. *La damoiselle élue.* Trial proof of the original color lithograph by Maurice Denis which was used as the book's cover. Inscribed by Debussy in ink, upper right, with a quatrain by Pierre Louÿs:

> *Parmi les champs d'anis*
> *portant la fleur d'absinthe*
> *je suis la femme peinte*
> *par Maurice Denis.*
>> *(P. L.)*

Across the bottom of the proof Debussy has written in pencil the name and and address of the (intended) publisher.

158. *Chansons de Bilitis. (Pierre LOUYS). CLAUDE DEBUSSY. 1. La Flûte de Pan. 2. La Chevelure. 3. Le Tombeau des Naïades.* Paris: Eugène Fromont, Éditeur. Inscribed:

> *pour Madame Lucien Fontaine. / et qu'elle permette d'insinuer / que ce même cahier contient le / meilleur de mon affectueux dévouement. / 14 Août 99 / Claude Debussy.*

159. *Pelléas et Mélisande. Drame lyrique en 5 actes et 12 tableaux de Maurice Maeterlinck. Musique de Claude Debussy. Partition pour Chant et Piano.* Paris: Fromont, 1902. 4to, contemporary cloth of *Art Nouveau* floral motifs, top edges gilt.

First edition. Large-paper copy on *papier Japon* (limited to 50 copies), with the following inscription from Debussy to Albert Carré, who produced *Pelléas* at the Opéra-Comique:

> *à Monsieur A. Carré / et plus encore à l'artiste qui sut créer / l'atmosphère de rêve inoubliable sans laquelle / Pelléas et Mélisande n'auraient pu vivre. / Claude Debussy / Mai / 1902*

The opera was dedicated to the memory of Debussy's late publisher, Georges Hartmann, and to the composer André Messager. Messager is listed here as "Directeur de la musique" and it was he who conducted the orchestra at the première on 30 April 1902. This copy was used by Messager during the rehearsals and bears corrections, annotations, and other markings in his hand on about forty pages.

. . . Debussy was continually taking back his score for improvement. Of the work in its final stages we know only that André Messager, who conducted the first performance, was its champion and that Debussy initiated him into each section of the work as he rewrote it. But even on the eve of the rehearsals there were sections that had still to be revised.

> *Debussy* by Lockspeiser.
> London & New York, 1936, pages 56–57.

It was, in fact, Messager who had suggested to Carré, after having heard Debussy sing and play *Pelléas* before a small group of friends who had gathered at the house of Pierre Louÿs, that he produce *Pelléas* at the Opéra-Comique.

Toward the end of 1901, at the home of Maeterlinck and his wife, the singer Georgette Leblanc, Debussy played his score for *Pelléas*. Mme. Leblanc was so taken by the beauty of the prelude for the death of Mélisande that Maeterlinck urged Debussy to assign the role of Mélisande to her. Debussy agreed. Mme. Leblanc rehearsed the role five times at Debussy's apartment and at her own. Then one day she read in the paper that Debussy had engaged Mary Garden for the role. Maeterlinck was furious and there was talk of a duel. But it came to nothing. Maeterlinck brought suit. Unfortunately for him, however, he had given Debussy, in their contract, authorization to put on the opera as he, Debussy, saw fit. The suit was thrown out of court.

Before bringing suit formally, Maeterlinck had made a final appeal to Albert Carré, insisting that the role of Mélisande be restored to his wife or that the opera be withdrawn from the schedule of the Opéra-Comique. Laid in this copy is Maeterlinck's original letter to Carré (Paris, 15 January 1902) in which he presents his complaints and his ultimatum. He carefully avoids using Debussy's name, referring to him only as "my collaborator." Also included is a letter from Maeterlinck to Carré, undated but from a happier period of their relationship, in which Maeterlinck writes:

> . . . I shall never forget the pure and profound artistic emotion you have helped me to experience. Thanks to you I have seen come alive a poem that I thought was incapable of being dramatized. It is the first time I have known that joy and I thank you for it with all my heart . . . .

Bound in are seven contemporary photographs by Tabourin of the original sets for *Pelléas* by Jusseaume and Ronsin. Tipped in is the menu of the supper given at the Café Riche after the 100th performance.

Also laid in are a letter from Debussy to Carré in which Debussy cites a phrase of Arkel's (Pelléas's grandfather), and a photograph of Pierre Louÿs seated at his harmonium. It was with the collaboration of Louÿs and this harmonium that Debussy gave the first reading of *Pelléas* to that small group of friends.

160. *Pelléas et Mélisande*. Another copy, this one not on Japan paper, donated by Debussy during World War I to a charity sale held to raise money to buy clothing for prisoners of war and inscribed by him:

> *Pour l'Oeuvre "Le Vêtement du Prisonnier de Guerre" / Hommage sympathique / Claude Debussy, / Décembre 1916.*

The copy was bought by Debussy's friend, the music critic Émile Vuillermoz. The dedication page is covered by an original drawing in pen-and-ink and watercolor.

161. Holograph music manuscript, 4 pp. Folio. Sketches for *Pelléas et Mélisande*.

162. 21 holograph letters signed (2 on his carte-de-visite) to Émile Vuiller-moz, 1912–1916. ". . . As for Maeterlinck's card, I need a little briefing. . . . Couldn't you drop by the house for a minute? In general I don't much like mistakes. In particular, I'm afraid of Maeterlinck's!"

163. Vellum-backed green-cloth folding case, gold-stamped on front cover "Pelléas et Mélisande," and on backstrip "Claude Debussy." With green silk ties. Measures 16¼" x 12¼".

This is the case in which Debussy kept the manuscript of *Pelléas et Mélisande* during the years he was working on it. Inside the back cover the case is inscribed in green crayon, in Debussy's hand: "Composition / Commencée en Décembre 93 / Terminée en Août 95 / Orchestration."

164. Documents relating to *Pelléas et Mélisande*: rehearsal notice issued to Debussy by the Opéra-Comique; ticket for the dress rehearsal; ticket and menu for the supper celebrating the 100th performance (28 January 1913); programme of the Gala Claude Debussy (19 June 1913), with a lecture by Vuillermoz and with Debussy playing his music; ticket for the reprise of *Pelléas et Mélisande* at the Opéra-Comique on 14 December 1962.

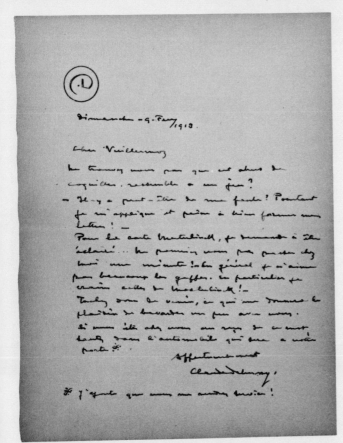

168

171

165. *L'Enfance de Pelléas. Lettres de Claude Debussy à André Messager re-cueuillies et annotées par Jean André-Messager. Preface d'Émile Vuillermoz.* Paris: Dorbon-Aîné [1938]. 4to, original wrappers, uncut and unopened.

Copy No. 1 of an edition limited to 330, all on *papier vélin à la forme de Vincent Montgolfier.*

166. *L'Enfance de Pelléas.* Maquette, including typescript and corrected proofs.

167. Holograph letter signed from Georgette Leblanc-Maeterlinck, asking Debussy's permission to give a charity performance of *Pelléas et Mélisande* at the Abbaye de St.-Wandrille, with M. Bernard singing the role of Golaud.

168. Original terra-cotta mask of Debussy by the French sculptor Louise Ochsé. Measures 10″ x 7″. Signed on back "L. Ochsé."

This mask of Debussy was commissioned by Gabriel Astruc, the impresario who had earlier brought Diaghilev's *Ballets Russes* to Paris and whose dream was to make his Théâtre des Champs-Élysées the home of French music. In 1932 the international Debussy festival was held there, under the presidency of André Messager. Orchestras directed by Toscanini, Pierné, Gaubert, Weingartner, and Inghelbrecht played Act IV of *Pelléas* and extracts from other major works by Debussy. A monument to Debussy by Jan and Joel Martel was unveiled in Paris. Another one was created by Aristide Maillol for St.-Germain-en-Laye, Debussy's birthplace. Mme. Ochsé's mask was, in a sense, the principal image of the Festival. Photographed by Laure Albin-Guillot and reproduced on the silver cover of the folio brochure commemorating the festival, it brought Debussy to life in a way that none of the monumental statuary could possibly do.

169. *Théâtre des Champs-Élysées—17 Juin 1932—Festival . . . Claude De-bussy. Programme et Livre d'Or des Souscripteurs.* The commemorative brochure referred to above. Folio, original illustrated silver wrappers.

170. *Claude Debussy* by Yvan Thiele. Soft-ground etching, inscribed:

3e état de Claude Debussy. Yvan Thiele, 1927.

MARCEL DUCHAMP

171. 12 holograph letters signed to Man Ray, 1929–1938. One of the letters bears a holograph note by Mary Callery and is co-signed by Salvador Dali.

Intimate correspondence between two of the prime movers of the modern movement. References to Kiki, Madame (Helen) Hessel, Miss (Katherine) Dreier, and Tristan Tzara.

172. *Marcel Duchamp* by Georges Hugnet. Paris: [privately printed] 1941. Small oblong 8vo. With an original illustration by Duchamp tipped in. 200 copies were issued.

173

173

174

ARRIVANT de la Cannebière, on
débouche sur le large quai de la
Fraternité, un des coins les plus
vivants de Marseille.

Là, depuis le comptoir du *Brû-
leur de Loups*, jusqu'à la salle pro-
vençale de Mistral, se succèdent sans interruption
bars et restaurants où l'on mange les fruits de mer. Là,
devant leur étalage humide, vous attendent écailleurs
d'huîtres, de praires, de moules et d'oursins; là, étalés

174

173. *Le Lièvre* and *Le Serpent*. Original wood engravings, proofs of the 2 *planches refusées* (1911).

In 1911 Dufy was commissioned by a Paris publisher named Deplanche to illustrate Apollinaire's *Le Bestiaire ou Cortège d'Orphée*. For it he engraved a series of woodcuts. Deplanche didn't approve of two of them—*Le Lièvre* and *Le Serpent*—and Dufy was obliged to do other versions of those two subjects. His second attempts were published, but it is the general consensus that they are not nearly so interesting as those that Deplanche rejected (and, consequently, did not publish). The published versions are more conventional. *Le Lièvre (The Hare)*, in particular, is cast in its second form in a kind of armorial style which makes it much less a departure from the sort of thing artists had already been doing in that medium than Dufy's first version of it, which is much fresher and more original.

The book, limited to an edition of 120 copies, is a kind of landmark in the history of modern graphic art. One French commentator wrote of it: "Par cette illustration, Dufy créa un nouveau style dans la gravure sur bois. C'est ici la source d'inspiration de tous les graveurs modernes."

174. *La Belle Enfant ou l'Amour à Quarante Ans* by Eugène Montfort. Paris: Ambroise Vollard, 1930. Illustrated by Dufy with 110 original etchings, full page and throughout the text. 4to, full aubergine crushed levant with decorative pattern of beige morocco inlays in motif of marine fauna appropriate to the story; interior morocco borders with similar mosaic and gold-stamped pattern, doublures and endleaves of harmonizing suede, all edges gilt, within morocco-edged sleeve and slipcase (binding by Madeleine Gras). One of 245 numbered copies on *vélin d'Arches*. (Johnson, 53; Skira, 107.)

Dufy's illustration of *La Belle Enfant* of Eugène Montfort may be considered his most perfect and most ingenious work—more colorful, even, in its black-and-white etchings than the color lithographs of his *Tartarin*.

> *Vingt-deux artistes du livre* by Mornand.
> Paris [1948], page 149.

ANDRÉ DUNOYER DE SEGONZAC

175. 82 holograph letters and cards, with related documents, addressed to Jean-Gabriel Daragnès and his wife Janine, 1920–1967.

One of the masterworks of modern French book production, Charles-Louis Philippe's *Bubu de Montparnasse*, illustrated with original etchings by Segonzac, was printed in the Daragnès atelier. A number of the letters in this correspondence are concerned with the details of that edition; others, with Segonzac's editions of *Les Géorgiques*, Colette's *La Treille muscate*, and Roland Dorgelès's *Les Croix de bois*, *La Boule de gui*, and *Le Cabaret de la belle femme*, in which Daragnès also collaborated.

176. *Dunoyer de Segonzac* by Paul Jamot. Paris: Floury, 1929. 4to, original pictorial wrappers, uncut.

One of 200 deluxe copies printed on Japan paper, with four original etchings and a proof state of the cover before letters. Inscribed:

> *Pour mon vieux / Gabriel Daragnès / camarade de combat / de mes débuts dans les / Croix de Bois—et / très bel artiste et grand / Ami / A. D. de Segonzac.*

PAUL ÉLUARD

177. 185 holograph letters signed, written to his parents and to his "first friend," the binder A.-J. Gonon, publisher of Éluard's book *Le Devoir et l'inquiétude.* This group of letters covers the years 1911–1919, about 315 pp.

At the beginning of the correspondence, Éluard is 16 and is still using the name Paul-Eugène Grindel. All his life in delicate health, he is in Switzerland on vacation in the summer of 1912 when he begins to cough up blood and is obliged to remain in a sanatorium near Davos for about a year and a half. There he meets a young Russian girl, Gala (Helena Dmitrovnie Diakonova) who becomes his fiancée. She returns to Russia in 1914 and is prevented by the outbreak of war from returning to Paris as they had planned. Finally she is able to arrange her return to France to wait out the war in Paris because they are planning marriage by the end of 1916.

Exposition internationale Paris 1937

Manifestations littéraires — Poésie
Le Samedi 2 Octobre à 16 H 15

☆

Conférence de Paul Eluard

"AVENIR DE LA POÉSIE"

Lectures :

Petrus Borel, Charles Baudelaire, Gérard de Nerval, ~~Charles~~ Lautréamont, Arthur Rimbaud, ~~Germain~~ Charles Cros, Alfred Jarry, Maurice ~~Maeterlinck~~, Saint-Pol Roux, Guillaume Apollinaire, Pierre Reverdy, ~~André Breton~~ ~~André Breton~~ Pierre-Jean Jouve, André Breton, Tristan Tzara, Paul Eluard, Henri Michaux Benjamin Péret, René Char, Pablo Picasso.

181

Après moi le sommeil   à Max Ernst

2

J'entrai dans cet état qui joue sa fin

~~1~~ 1

Au déclin de la force
Un feu très sombre déambule

3

Corbeaux mêmes minuits rapaces
Dentelle à ternir tous les ors

4

Par brassées de murmures la lande et ses fantômes
Répétaient les discours dont je m'étourdissais

5

Lys de cire et les chênes moisis
A l'odeur de ~~la~~ cellier ~~assid~~
Carré d'étoiles vertes
Les oiseaux desséchés
Prenaient des poses immortelles.

Le premier joue de la souple
~~Vont~~ me lavée de son venin.

~~Les~~ Plusieurs douceurs entrevues
toute plus mignonnes
Que le cri de la fleur amie
Avaient fondre dans la nuit
Comme clefs dans leur serrure
Comme boissons dans la chaleur.

182

Before entering the Army, Éluard had had two small books of poems printed at his own expense—*Premiers poèmes* and *Dialogues des inutiles*. The poems that grow out of his wartime experience take their first form in a 12-page mimeographed pamphlet entitled *Le Devoir*, of which he prints 17 copies in the summer of 1916. Most of these he sends to Gonon for distribution. As the poems increase in number, he arranges with Gonon for a book to be called *Le Devoir et l'inquiétude*, which will include the first wartime poems, 11 new ones and a group of prose poems to which he gives the title *Le Rire d'un autre*. In July 1917, Gonon has an edition of 206 copies printed, illustrated with a woodcut by André Deslignières.

As the end of the war moves into sight, Éluard writes to Gonon: "We are going to fight for happiness, after having fought for life." He has now printed his *Poèmes pour la paix* in the form of a broadside and sends him a copy. But his elation is tempered: "I am writing somber poems . . . as somber as nothingness . . . . I have been greatly shaken by the death of Apollinaire . . . . No one will give what he endlessly promised . . . ."

The final letters show Éluard "stronger and more intelligent" (a prediction he applied to all at the time of the Armistice). Although not demobilized until mid-1919, he is already moving into the new life that will take him to the center and one of the peaks of the French literary world of the twenties and thirties. He is writing of Gonzague-Frick and Dujardin, Ozenfant and Lhote, Derain and Lurçat and Adrienne Monnier. Dada and Surrealism lie just ahead.

178. *Le Devoir et l'inquiétude. Poèmes, suivis de Le Rire d'un autre. Ornés d'une gravure sur bois par André Deslignières.* Paris: Chez A.-J. Gonon, 1917. 12mo, original marbled wrappers, uncut.

First edition of Éluard's first published book. Edition limited to 206 copies numbered and signed (with his initials) by Gonon. Printed on the hand press of Léon Pichon.

179. Holograph letter (draft) to Vicomte Charles de Noailles, a frequent contributor to surrealist causes, soliciting funds to complete publication of the review *Le Surréalisme au service de la révolution*.

180. Autograph manuscript of definitions prepared by Éluard (and André Breton) for the *Dictionnaire abrégé du surréalisme*, but not published, 37 pp. 8vo. One of the sheets contains an entry in Breton's hand; another has one each by Breton and Éluard.

181. *Avenir de la poésie.* Holograph manuscript, 6 pp. Folio. Outline and notes for the lecture given by Éluard on 2 October 1937, at the Exposition Internationale, Paris.

182. *Après moi le sommeil.* Holograph manuscript, 2 pp. Small 4to. An early, corrected version of one of Éluard's finest poems, dedicated to Max Ernst.

183. *A Francis Poulenc.* Holograph manuscript poem, with corrections, 2 pp. From the collection *De la musique encore et toujours* (1946). On the verso of the second sheet are two lines of another poem. Poulenc set a number of Éluard's poems to music.

184. *Cette année-là comme les autres nous avions besoin de contes.* Holograph manuscript. Preface for a book by Lise Deharme.

185. *Victor Hugo.* Holograph manuscript, signed. Éluard writes here as a patriot, but with one eye on Moscow.

186. *Je suis l'homme qui échoue.* Holograph manuscript poem, unpublished.

187. Manuscript copy, in Éluard's hand, of 3 poems by Pierre Louÿs; added notation in the hand of Georges Hugnet.

188. Sketch for a portrait of Paul Éluard by Valentine Hugo. Pencil. Measures 11¼″ x 5″. Éluard died in November 1952. Valentine Hugo did this portrait for a memorial number of *Les Cahiers du Sud* published early in 1953.

LÉON-PAUL FARGUE

189. *Tancrède.* Paris, 1911. 8vo, full green boards, original wrappers bound in, uncut (binding by Gonon).

> First edition of Fargue's rarest book, limited to 200 numbered copies on *papier vergé d'Arches*. One of a few first-issue copies with the complete text. Presentation copy inscribed:
>
> > *A Mademoiselle Raymonde Linossier / Léon-Paul Fargue / confrère en vivisme.*
>
> Under the title, on both title-page and wrapper, Fargue has written "(1893–1894)." On the limitation page he has written his name. Daragnès bookplate.
> Mlle. Linossier was a close friend of Fargue, Sylvia Beach, Poulenc, Milhaud, and Satie. It was she who took over the typing of the Circe episode in *Ulysses* to break the bottleneck which had halted Darantière's printing of the book. After that, Joyce told Sylvia Beach that he had "put Raymonde into *Ulysses*."
> Fargue wrote *Tancrède*, which he later referred to as a "lyrical novel," in class when he was 15. The manuscript was confiscated by his teacher, a Monsieur Vautier, who, after reading it, was so impressed with its quality that he returned it to Fargue. It was first published in 1895 in the Franco-German deluxe review *Pan*, with illustrations by Launay, Bottini, and Delcourt. Sixteen years later Valery Larbaud underwrote its publication in book form.

190. *Poèmes.* Paris: Éditions de la Noùvelle Revue Française, 1912. 4to, full green boards, original wrappers bound in (binding by Gonon).

> First edition, copy imprinted "Exemplaire spécialement tiré pour Verbeke." On the half-title is a presentation inscription from Fargue to Raymonde Linossier and a four-line holograph poem signed by Fargue. Daragnès bookplate.
> In a letter to Lucien Descaves of the Goncourt Academy, submitting this book for the Prix Goncourt, Fargue wrote, "I have tried to achieve . . . a new prose

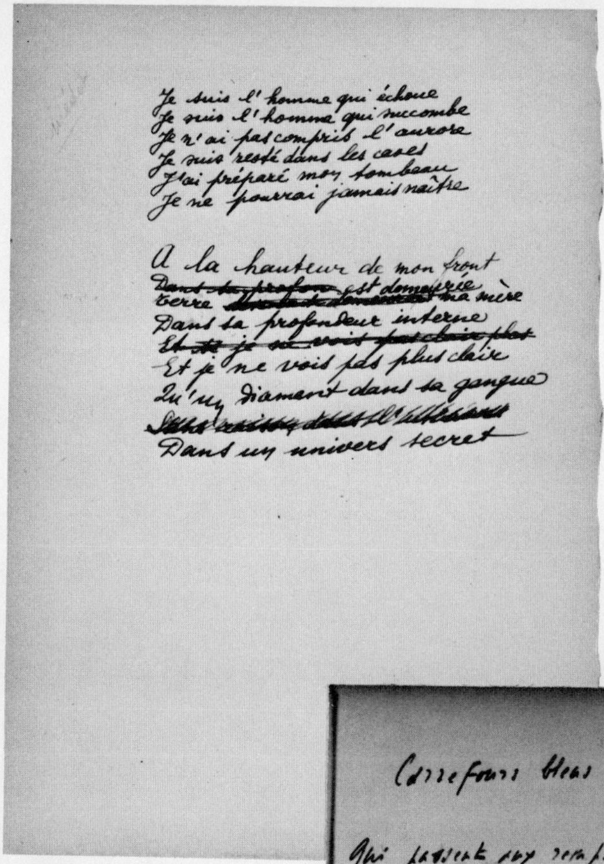

Je suis l'homme qui échoue
Je suis l'homme qui succombe
Je n'ai pas compris l'aurore
Je suis resté dans les caves
J'ai préparé mon tombeau
Je ne pourrai jamais naître

A la hauteur de mon front
~~Dans sa profon~~ est domiciliée
terre ma mère
Dans sa profondeur interne
~~Et je ne vois pas plus clair~~
Et je ne vois pas plus claire
Qu'un diamant dans sa gangue
Dans un univers secret

186

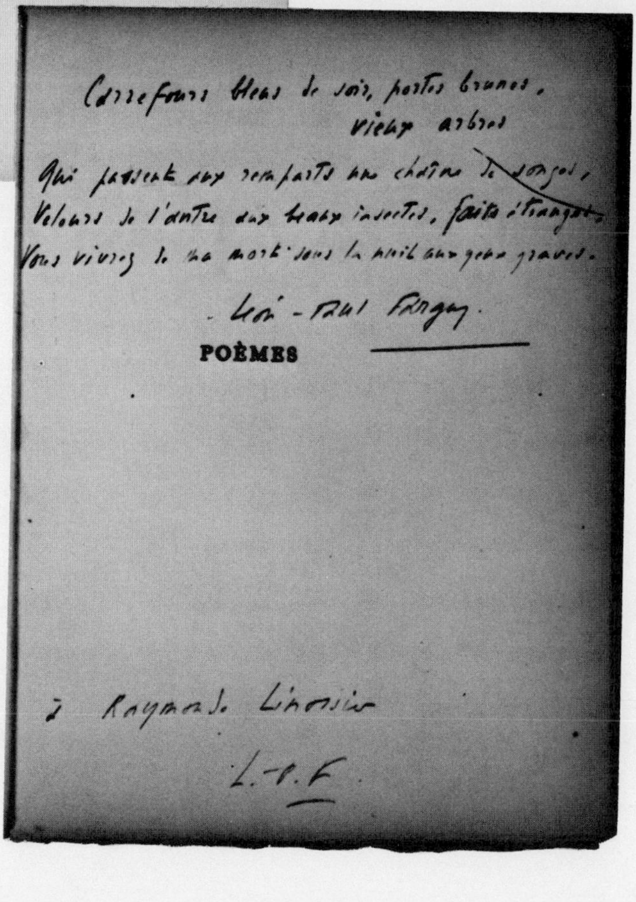

Carrefours bleus du soir, portes brunes,
vieux arbres
Qui passent aux remparts une chaîne de songes,
Velours de l'antre aux beaux insectes, faits étrangers,
Vous vivrez de ma mort sous la nuit aux yeux graves.

Léon-Paul Fargue

POÈMES

à Raymonde Linossier

L.-P. F.

190

— notes sur Bernard —

En 86 en effet B. vint à Pont
Aven après avoir visité minutieu-
sement l'exposition dernière des
impressionistes Rue Laffitte. Il
quitta alors les chairs de tout
le monde Pissarro Manet et
Gauguin pour adopter ce qui
venait de surgir de plus neuf,
le petit point. Il laissait cette
année chez Gloanec à Pont Aven
un panneau exactement semblable
à un Seurat (il y est toujours).
à ce moment Gauguin de toutes
ses forces combattait toutes
les complications sans avoir

form which maintains a balance between plastic form and musical form, between a painter's vision and rhythm." Fargue saw this book as continuing the tradition of "Baudelaire's prose poems, certain pages of Nerval, Aloysius Bertrand's *Gaspard de la nuit*, Laforgue's *Moralités légendaires*, Mallarmé's *Divagations* . . . ."

191. *Pour la musique. Poèmes.* [Paris] Éditions de la Nouvelle Revue Française [1914]. 4to, original wrappers, uncut. First edition, on heavy handmade *vergé* paper. Daragnès bookplate. Inscribed:

> à l'Abbé Léonce Petit / son ami / Léon-Paul Fargue.

192. *Pour la musique. Poèmes.* Another copy, this one on Japan paper. 4to, full green boards, original wrappers bound in (binding by Gonon). This copy, which has no title-page, is apparently a proof copy. The colophon gives the date of its printing as one month earlier than that given in the preceding copy. Daragnès bookplate. Inscribed:

> à Mademoiselle Raymonde Linossier / avec reconnaissance / Léon-Paul Fargue.

193. *Pour la musique.* Holograph manuscript signed, bound in one volume, 20 pp. 4to, full green boards (binding by Gonon). At the end of the first poem is a presentation inscription to Raymonde Linossier. The first poem and the final one, a prose poem, are not included in the published version. Also bound in are seven pages of proof from the book, corrected by Fargue. Daragnès bookplate.

194. *Portrait de Léon-Paul Fargue* by Paul-Émile Bécat. One of 200 signed proofs. Original etching by the brother-in-law of Adrienne Monnier at whose bookshop, La Maison des Amis des Livres, located across the street from Sylvia Beach's Shakespeare and Company, Fargue was one of the more active literary lions.

PAUL GAUGUIN

195. *Notes sur Bernard.* Holograph manuscript concerning the work of Émile Bernard, the Pont Aven group, and the Synthetist movement, 5 pp.

Writing in the third person, Gauguin seems determined to cut Émile Bernard down to size; shows him to be an imitator of Pissarro, Manet, and Gauguin, then Seurat and Cézanne, and finally Gauguin again.

> . . . Ah, Monsieur Bernard, instead of suggesting that you adopt a personality that you will never have, build a body of work that will remain true to itself and you won't leave yourself open to be looked upon as a fraud by a whole generation of painters who have watched you since your beginnings at Pont Aven . . . .

196. *Portrait de Stéphane Mallarmé*. Original etching, [18]91. Signed "P Go" and dated "91" in the plate. The only etching executed by Gauguin. (Guérin 14, second state.)

Gauguin greatly admired Mallarmé. After Mallarmé's death, Gauguin wrote to Daniel Monfreid from Papeete (12 December 1898):

> I have read in the *Mercure* of the death of Stéphane Mallarmé and have been greatly saddened by it. One more who has died a martyr to art: his life is at least as admirable as his work.

One of the great portraits of the period. Poe's raven is shown looking over Mallarmé's left shoulder. (Poe's preeminence in France ever since the mid-nineteenth century is due in good part to the fact that Baudelaire and Mallarmé were among his principal translators.)

197. *Haute surveillance*. Paris, 1947. 8vo, original wrappers, uncut and mostly unopened, in cardboard case.

First edition of Genet's rarest book, limited to 60 copies, on *papier Lana de Docelles*, printed for Les Cinéastes-Bibliophiles. This copy belonged to the actor-director Léon Mathot, whose name is printed on the limitation page and whose name and address Genet has written on the slipcase.

198. *Haute surveillance*. [Paris] Gallimard (1949). 8vo, original wrappers, uncut and unopened. First published edition. Review copy inscribed:

A *Monsieur Gabriel Marcel / avec mon admiration / Jean Genet.*

Publisher's descriptive broadsheet laid in.

199. *Haute surveillance. Édition définitive.* [Paris] Gallimard (1965). 8vo, original wrappers, uncut. First printing of the revised edition.

200. *Haute surveillance.* Four holograph manuscripts of the play, in varying forms, 60–100 pp. each. Two of them bear the definitive title, and two of them the earlier title *Pour la belle.* Two are dated "décembre, 1946," and three are signed by Genet. All contain many corrections and deletions.

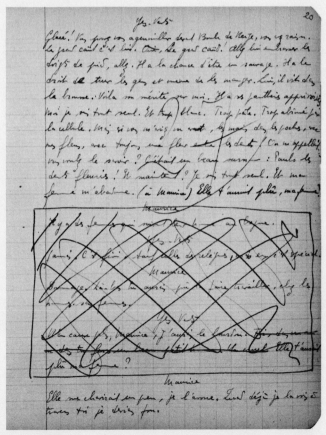

201. *Notre-Dame-des-Fleurs. Roman.* Monte-Carlo: Aux dépens d'un amateur [1942]. 4to, original wrappers, uncut and unopened, in slipcase. First edition, limited to 350 numbered copies.

202. *Notre-Dame des Fleurs. Roman.* [Lyon] L'Arbalète [1948]. Square 12mo, original wrappers, uncut. Second edition, printed on the hand press of Marc Barbezat, in a limited edition for subscribers. Daragnès bookplate.

203. *Notre-Dame-des-Fleurs. Roman.* [Lyon] Barbezat [1966]. 12mo, original wrappers, uncut. Third edition, the first to be placed on sale openly.

204. *Notre-Dame-des-Fleurs.* Complete manuscript, holograph and corrected typescript, of the book that is considered Genet's masterpiece, 198 pp. 4to, with an additional 30 pieces of manuscript pinned to the numbered pages. Given by Genet to Jean Cocteau and kept by him in a manila folder bearing the name of his brother, Paul Cocteau. The brother's name is crossed out and the book's title written above it.

> Genet wrote this book while imprisoned at La Santé. The first fifty pages were written on sheets of brown paper from which prisoners fashioned paper bags. A jailer discovered Genet's manuscript, and it was destroyed by the prison authorities. After three days' solitary confinement for misuse of prison property, Genet began again to write his novel.
>
> It is not known how he managed, from a prison cell, to find a publisher or deliver the manuscript to him or who the "amateur" (see entry 201 above) was who paid for the book's publication. It has been suggested that Cocteau, who intervened publicly and privately several times in 1942 and 1943 in Genet's behalf, may have played a role in the affair. The presence of this manuscript in Cocteau's collection lends support to that theory. It was this book that launched Genet's reputation as a major writer.

205. *La Galère*. Holograph manuscript signed, 6pp. With a presentation inscription from Genet to Cocteau:

> *Mon cher Jean puisque je ne pourrai pas te dédier officiellement / mes poèmes, laisse-moi t'offrir la copie de celui-ci / Ton ami / Jean Genet.*

206. 6 holograph letters signed to Jean Cocteau. Small 4to and 8vo. Written from prison, concerning the conditions of his imprisonment (no bed to sleep on); his cell-mates; his attempts to write in the overcrowded cells (*Miracle de la rose*); his dissatisfaction with *Notre-Dame-des-Fleurs*.

207. 289 holograph letters signed and 37 related documents addressed to Eugène Rouart, 1896–1936.

> Gide met Eugène Rouart at the home of the sculptor Jean-Paul Laurens, whose son, Paul-Albert, had been Gide's traveling companion on a trip to Tunis in October 1893. During this trip, Gide began to write *Les Nourritures terrestres.* Rouart soon became one of Gide's closest friends and in 1895, when *Paludes* was published, it was dedicated to him.
>
> This is one of the most important Gide correspondences still unpublished.

208. Holograph letter signed to the Belgian writer Maurice des Ombiaux, 5 pp. Des Ombiaux had made, first in conversation with Gide and later in a published review, certain criticisms of *Paludes*, notably the idea—launched and relaunched with the publication of most of Gide's works—that Gide was a bad influence on the young. In this letter Gide amiably rejects the sinister role attributed to him, not without a certain characteristic jesuitical ambivalence.

209. 12 letters, 11 of them holograph, to the Paris bookseller Camille Bloch, 1917–1920. Concerning Gide's purchases of books from him and sale, through him, of certain of the manuscripts and first editions of his works.

210. *Lettre ouverte à M. Francis Jammes.* Typescript signed with holograph postscript, on the letterhead of the *Nouvelle Revue Française*, 24 April 1923.

> Gide takes issue with Jammes's published account of Gide's early relations with Paul Claudel, and with a "poetic description" of his family environment which Gide characterizes as "charming" but far from authentic.

211. 70 holograph letters to Gide's friend and occasional collaborator Pierre Herbart, author of *A la recherche d'André Gide* (Paris: Gallimard, 1952), 1929–1951, 160 sides. Together with a copy of a letter from Gide to Jef Last.

> Many details concerning *Les Caves du Vatican, Isabelle, Saül, Robert ou l'intérêt général,* and other works of Gide, his Communism and disillusioning trip to Russia, his travels to Germany, Italy, Morocco, and elsewhere. Discussions of Cocteau, Jean Desbordes, Malraux, Simon and Dorothy Bussy, Louis Jouvet, Jean-Louis Barrault, John Lehmann, Roger Martin du Gard, E. R. Curtius, Jean Paulhan, Julien Benda, Ilya Ehrenburg, Camus, Eugène Dabit, and others.

212. *Feuilles de route. 1895–1896.* Brussels: Imprimerie V. Vandersypen, 1899. 16mo, three-quarter maroon crushed levant, top edges gilt, original wrappers bound in (binding by Huser). Rare first edition, of which only a small number of copies were printed.

> The book is divided into two parts, and in this copy Gide has corrected, in ink, the entire second part (two-thirds of the book). Printer's corrections, in pencil, are also present. Gide's corrections do not appear in the edition of the collected works published by Gallimard.

213. *Dostoievsky d'après sa correspondance.* Corrected proofs of an article published in the 25 May 1908 issue of *La Grande Revue*, 26 pp.

214. *Isabelle. Récit.* Paris: Éditions de la Nouvelle Revue Française, Marcel Rivière et Cie., 1911. 12mo, original blue wrappers, uncut. A fine copy of the rare first printing of the first edition. Five hundred copies were printed, on *vergé d'Arches*, but Gide had the printing destroyed because of its typographical irregularities. Only about ten copies survived and these bear, on the colophon, the printing date of 29 May. A new, corrected printing of 500 copies, also on *vergé d'Arches*, was issued on 20 June.

215. *Isabelle.* Typescript signed, with holograph corrections, 99 pp. Label inscribed in Gide's hand on Nouvelle Revue Française wrapper:

> *Dactylographie complète / d'Isabelle / avec les corrections et les deux versions / de la fin.*

The second ending (8 pp.) included in the typescript is unpublished.

216. *Isabelle.* Corrected proofs for most of the book, bound in 2 volumes, three-quarter morocco, raised bands, top edges gilt.

217. *Le Journal des Faux-monnayeurs.* Paris: Éditions Eos, 1926. Small 4to, original wrappers, uncut. First edition. One of 25 numbered author's copies of a total edition of 561, with the following inscription to Gide's brother-in-law:

> *à Marcel Drouin / son frère et ami / André Gide.*

Printed in two colors by Coulouma.

218. *Le Journal des Faux-monnayeurs.* Holograph manuscript, 132 pp. Folio and small 4to. Written in 2 notebooks, with additional text on loose sheets tipped into the larger of the two. Nearly one-fourth of this text was eliminated from this book but was printed in Gide's novel *Les Faux-monnayeurs* (1925). There are a number of differences between this manuscript and the printed text. From the library of Paul Voûte, with his bookplate.

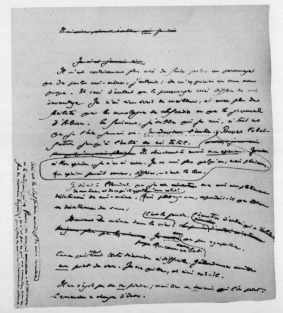

218

219. *L'École des femmes*. Paris: Éditions de la Nouvelle Revue Française, 1929. 12mo, original blue wrappers, uncut. First edition. One of 547 numbered copies on *papier de Hollande van Gelder*.

220. *Robert. Supplément à l'École des femmes*. Paris: Éditions de la Nouvelle Revue Française, 1930. 4to, original wrappers, uncut and unopened.

First edition. One of 123 numbered large-paper copies on *papier vergé*, this one "imprimé pour M. Milich," according to an imprint on the limitation page. With the bookplate of Michel Bollori, whose outstanding Gide collection was dispersed at public sale in Paris in 1954.

221. *Robert. Supplément à l'École des femmes*. A review copy, regular 8vo format. Inscribed by Gide:

> *à Eugène Rouart / son vieux* [sic] *ami / André Gide.*

L'École des femmes, written in 1927 and 1928 and published in 1929, was concerned with the problems of marriage at a period when Gide was having problems with his own. The critical approval it received induced him to write and quickly publish a sequel—*Robert*—which he managed to turn out in one week in September 1929.

222. *L'École des femmes*. Holograph manuscript in two parts, the first written in a black cloth-bound folio daybook; the second, on sheets of deep pink bound into a morocco-backed notebook of marbled boards. The manuscript is complete in two parts, as in the printed version. The title is inscribed in Gide's hand at the beginning of the large daybook as "Geneviève ou l'École des Femmes." Beneath that is a dedication to Edmond Jaloux. The text of the first part covers 19 folio sheets in the daybook, written in a minute but very legible hand. Twenty additional sheets of manuscript have been laid in. This first part corresponds fairly closely to the first 83 pages of the printed text.

The text of the second part seems to be the first draft, with many additions and deletions, and it differs greatly from the published version, although it follows the essential lines of the narrative. The second part of the manuscript corresponds to pages 87 through the end (page 171) of the original edition. There are forty 4to pages of manuscript in the rose-colored sheets plus six large white folio sheets mounted on stubs and folded twice, and two sheets of corrected typescript.

223. *Robert. Supplément à l'École des femmes*. Holograph manuscript, 55 pp. Written in a notebook of 48 bound sheets. Small 4to. The preface is written on two separate sheets. This is the complete manuscript, in first draft, with numerous additions, deletions, and variant passages. The dedication, in the form of a letter to E. R. Curtius, takes up the two manuscript sheets laid in and was cut to two lines in the printed version. Inside the front cover Gide has made calculations concerning the ages of his characters.

224. *Robert ou l'intérêt général.* [*Pièce en cinq actes.*] *Lithographies de Maurice Brianchon.* Neuchâtel et Paris: Ides et Calendes (1949). Small 4to, original wrappers, uncut and unopened. First edition, forming Volume VI of the *Théâtre Complet d'André Gide.*

> From brief entries in his *Journal* we know that Gide began making notes for this play in the summer of 1934. It gave him a great deal of trouble, not least because his initial approach was to write it as a kind of Communist tract whose "realism" was essentially alien to him.
>
> Elsa Triolet translated the first version into Russian and a Moscow production was scheduled. But when Gide returned from Russia and published *Retour de l'U. R. S. S.,* his honeymoon with the Communist party was over and he decided to redo the play—"to transform this social conflict into a 'comedy of character.'" He thought so highly of some of the scenes that he kept trying to stitch them together in new ways, and that kept introducing new technical problems. Over a period of six years the play preoccupied him almost constantly. He finally published it in Algiers, in the review *L'Arche,* in 1944 and 1945. It was produced in Tunis at the Théâtre Municipal by a company called *L'Essor,* in April and May 1946.

225. *Robert, ou l'intérêt général.* Holograph manuscript in two versions, differing widely, 255 pp., plus a dozen sheets of related typescript. The first version is in sheets, in five acts; the second, in three bound notebooks, labeled Acts II, III, and IV.

226. Holograph letter signed from Francis Poulenc to Gide, 5 August [1940], 2 pp.

> Fleeing from Paris after the fall of France, Poulenc has had news of Gide from Henri de Montherlant in the "overpopulated . . . torrid" village where they have taken refuge. He associates Gide with the finest joys of his youth. He asks for news of Éluard, not only a dear friend, but "the very source of melodies which surely mean more to me than anything else." He writes of Auric, Paulhan, Mauriac, Milhaud.

227. 7 snapshots from the period of World War II, showing Gide in North Africa and Spain; some with the Dutch writer Jef Last.

EDMOND DE GONCOURT

228. *Le Mouvement naturaliste.* Holograph manuscript, 3 pp. Folio.

> Goncourt sees the Naturalist movement coming to an end by 1900, when it will be fifty years old. There will be a reaction against it but he doubts that Symbolism can take its place, because most of the Symbolists are poets.
>
> > . . . I ask myself if, in the nineteenth century, in this all-power of poetic prose, in this domination of the language by Chateaubriand and by Flaubert—I ask myself if a great intellectual movement can be led by versifiers.

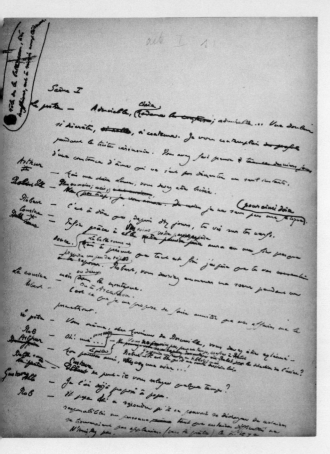

225

229

31 janvier 79.

Les idées du jour

Walt Whitman

Raoul Dufy

231

234

229. Holograph letter signed to Gustave Flaubert, 31 January 1879, 3 pp.

At a dinner at Charpentier's, Goncourt had heard that Flaubert had lost all his worldly goods and was about to be evicted from Croisset. Fortunately things had not reached that point. He discusses the success of the play made from Zola's novel *L'Assommoir* and speaks of his problems with the novel he is working on.

230. Holograph letter signed to Paul Verlaine, 4 June 1895. He sends Verlaine praise for *Confessions*, which he has just read, and thanks Verlaine for the article he has devoted to him in *Les Hommes du jour*.

REMY DE GOURMONT

231. 823 holograph manuscripts signed, totaling 1,636 pp. Essays written by Gourmont under the general title *Les Idées du jour* for the Paris paper *La France*, August 1911 to December 1913.

The finest critical mind in France in the early years of the century, Remy de Gourmont had been one of the founders and a principal collaborator of the *Mercure de France*. From then until his death, in September 1915, no pen was more influential than his—not only in French literary circles but for many British and Americans as well. In the Gourmont memorial issue of *The Little Review*, Ezra Pound wrote of him, "Gourmont prepared our era; behind him there stretches a limitless darkness." And years later he summed it all up when he wrote to a friend, "My generation needed Remy de Gourmont."

In *Les Idées du jour* Gourmont wrote about whatever was on his mind at the moment. The series gave a wide-ranging view of contemporary life with frequent reflections on writers and artists who interested him—Diderot, Stendhal, Flaubert, Whitman, Shaw, Renoir, and Rodin, among others.

232. *Les Reliques* [and] *Les Anti* . . . 2 manuscripts in the hand of Natalie Clifford Barney, Gourmont's "Amazon," with corrected proofs, 16 pp. Prepared for publication in *L'Éclair,* August–September 1891.

233. *Les Fleurs du Mal, Les Épaves* by Baudelaire. Autograph transcriptions signed, in the hand of Remy de Gourmont, 19 pp.

234. *Des Pensées inédites, avec dix-huit dessins de Raoul Dufy et une préface de Guillaume Apollinaire.* Paris: Éditions de la Sirène, 1920. 4to, loose in sheets within original boards, with ties.

Edition limited to 100 numbered copies. Illustrated with 18 portrait studies of Gourmont by Raoul Dufy. The text reproduces the holograph manuscripts of Apollinaire and Gourmont.

235. *Le Berceau de Gertrude Stein ou Le Mystère de la Rue de Fleurus.* Holograph manuscript, dated "Avril 1928," 8 pp. plus title-page. 4to.

236. *Christian Bérard et Pavel Tchelitchef.* Holograph manuscript, 13 pp. 4to. Bérard and Tchelitchev were among the artists who illustrated the deluxe, signed edition of Hugnet's translation of Gertrude Stein: *Dix portraits* (Paris, 1930).

237. *La Sphère de sable.* Holograph manuscript, 12 pp. 4to. Includes three unpublished poems which did not appear in the book, which was illustrated by Arp and privately printed by Robert Godet in 1943.

238. *Jean Arp.* Holograph manuscript, corrected, 14¼ pp.

239. *Jean Arp.* Typescript with holograph corrections and additions, 11⅛ pp. 4to.

240. *Non Vouloir.* Paris [privately printed], 1940. With an illustration by Miró. Small oblong 8vo, in folded sheet, as issued. One of a small number (200?) of copies.

241. *Non Vouloir.* Holograph manuscript, dated "15 mars—18 juin—Paris—Ste. Gemme," 4 pp. 4to.

242. *Ici la voix.* Holograph manuscripts of 17 prose poems appearing under the heading "Les Revenants futurs" in the book published by Seghers in

1954, containing a frontispiece by Picasso. Other materials related to these manuscripts are:

° Holograph manuscript signed, 3 pp. Not included in the published version.
° The first 17 pages of an early set of galleys, with holograph corrections.
° Complete set of corrected galleys and 4 pages of corrected typescript.
° Complete set of corrected page proofs.
° Proof of the *prière d'insérer*.

See also GERTRUDE STEIN, nos. 476, 479, 480, 481.

J.-K. HUYSMANS

243. 22 holograph letters and postcards, signed, addressed to Gustave Geffroy, covering the years 1885–1906 and including important contemporary details concerning the founding of the Goncourt Academy; together with holograph notes, 14 pp., by Huysmans relating to his work and methods of work. These pieces have been mounted and bound in one volume, small 4to, full brown crushed levant, raised bands, doublures and end-leaves of moiré, within slip-case (binding by Semet and Plumelle).

EUGÈNE IONESCO

244. *Propos sur mon théâtre et sur les propos des autres.* Holograph manuscript signed, with 10 pp. in corrected typescript, with extensive deletions, 43 pp. 4to.

> The text of a lecture delivered by Ionesco at the Sorbonne in March 1960—included in a somewhat different form in the collection *Notes et contre-notes* (Paris: Gallimard, 1962). He lashes out against theatrical realism, thesis-drama, and the "incoherence" and contradictions of his critics.

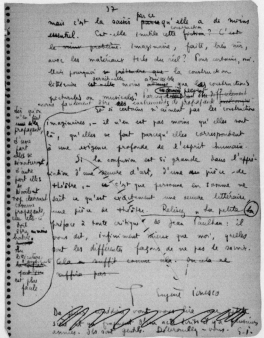

244

[illegible] 110

— Chapitre littéraire de l'Adultère chez les Adultes
ou de l'adultère adultéré —

Quand au ministère on reçut le télégramme annonçant
la chute du Phanérogame sur Honfleur on téléphona à l'Académie
qui se réunit en séance plénière. Le phanérogame était un
américain volant [illegible] giration acrobatique des [illegible] autour
du Bassin. Des délégués furent expédiés le soir même vers Honfleur.
C'était M. Trograngloxeul, médecin et esthète, [illegible]
[illegible]
directeur de l'Institut des Dégénérés supérieurs.
M. M. Psittacus et M. Hainabord, et enfin, je ne sais pourquoi
ni comment le phanérogame lui même. Dans la
nuit à cause du bruit de chaînes du torrentiel express, ces messieurs
ne dormirent pas, ils causèrent lentement. Les paroles qui y sont
prononcées ont été enlevées de la postérité par les [illegible] du chef de train.
On commença par des [illegible] métaphysiques pendant lesquelles
l'anglo-saxon [illegible] ennemis terribles; on finit
par des aperçus ingénieux sur les [illegible] qui durèrent douze heures du
trajet.

M. Trograngloxeul. Le besoin de symétrie a donné le jour à la philosophie
pour qui conçut l'homme comme reflet de l'univers c'est à dire comme
parallèle. Le besoin de symétrie prouverait que deux est à la base
du monde de sorte qu'il n'y aurait jamais destruction complète [illegible]
[illegible]

M. Psittacus. C'est la théorie [illegible]
du philosophe Tchou-hi.

M. Hainabord. On vous [illegible] avec vos propres arguments: notre
conception du zéro prouverait que zéro peut exister; la destruction complète
arrivera donc [illegible] D'ailleurs pourquoi le monde se reformerait-il
au moment précis que c'est la naissance de la matière et avant le zéro!

246

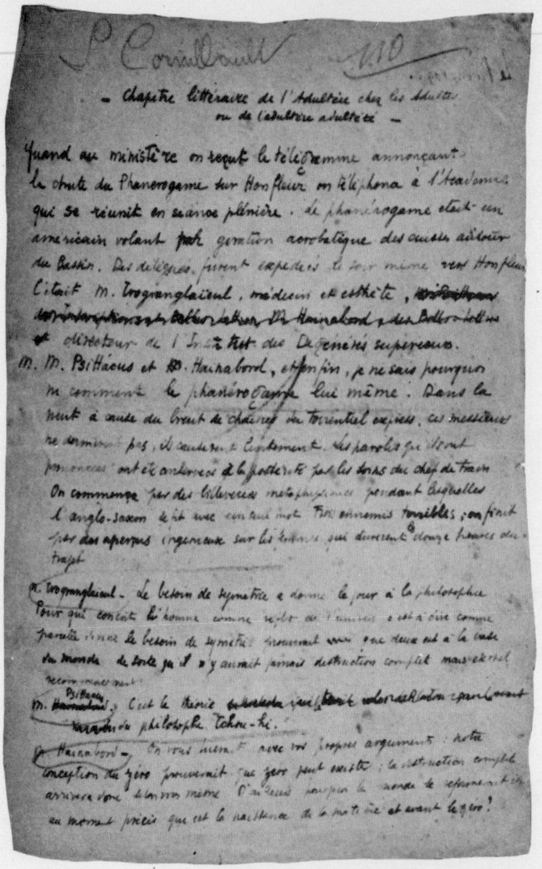

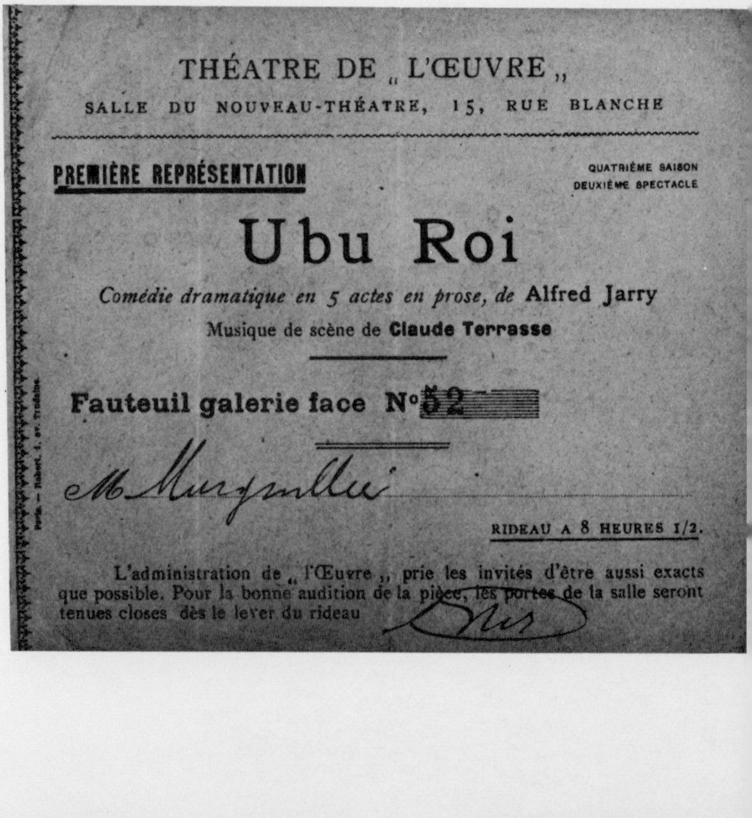

THÉATRE DE „ L'ŒUVRE „

SALLE DU NOUVEAU-THÉATRE, 15, RUE BLANCHE

PREMIÈRE REPRÉSENTATION

QUATRIÈME SAISON
DEUXIÈME SPECTACLE

Ubu Roi

Comédie dramatique en 5 actes en prose, de **Alfred Jarry**

Musique de scène de **Claude Terrasse**

Fauteuil galerie face N° 52

M Muhlfeld

RIDEAU A 8 HEURES 1/2.

L'administration de „ l'Œuvre „ prie les invités d'être aussi exacts que possible. Pour la bonne audition de la pièce, les portes de la salle seront tenues closes dès le lever du rideau

Paris. — Robert, 4, av. Trudaine.

252

245. *Le Phanérogame*. Paris, 1918. Square 12mo, original wrappers, uncut. First edition. Daragnès bookplate.

In Max Jacob's own one-line summary, this novel is a portrait from life of dilettantism in the period 1900–1905. But more than that, it is a characteristic anthology of the wittiest writer of his time.

246. *Le Phanérogame*. Holograph manuscript, 116 pp. Small folio.

The paper on which the manuscript was written reflects Max Jacob's extreme poverty. He could find no publisher for the book and had it printed himself (as he had done the year before with *Le Cornet à dés*). He sold what copies he could to his poor friends and to the occasional rich relation.

247. *Le Paradis, L'Enfer*, and *Danses d'avant-garde*. 3 holograph manuscripts with pen-and-ink sketches, including 3 self-portraits, 12 pp.

248. Photograph of Max Jacob, ca. 1910.

ALFRED JARRY

249. *La Passion. Les Clous du Seigneur*. Holograph manuscript, 3 1-3 pp. Folio. An early draft of the article by Jarry which appeared under this title in Remy de Gourmont's review *L'Ymagier*, No. 4, July 1895. With material not included in the published version.

250. *César Antéchrist*. Paris: Mercure de France, 1895. With 14 woodcut illustrations, including the first representation of Ubu. 12mo, full black crushed levant, doublures of citron levant, end-leaves of black silk, raised bands, gilt edges, original wrappers bound in, uncut, in slipcase. (binding by P.-L. Martin).

First edition. Pages 35–139 ("Acte terrestre") carry the first version of *Ubu Roi*. The edition was limited to 206 copies. This is one of 7 large-paper copies on *vergé Ingres de carnation*. It bears the following inscription in Jarry's hand:

Exemplaire de Marcel Schwob / Alfred Jarry.

When *Ubu Roi* appeared in its final form the following year, it was dedicated to Marcel Schwob.

251. 21 holograph letters signed to Lugné-Poe, written during the period when Jarry was serving as his secretary at the Théâtre de l'Oeuvre. Included is the letter (8 January 1896) in which Jarry proposes that Lugné-Poe produce *Ubu Roi* and outlines his ideas for all principal aspects of the production.

252. Ticket for the première of *Ubu Roi*, 10 December 1896.

253. Holograph letter signed to Henry Bauër, the influential drama critic of *L'Écho de Paris*, 15 December 1896, 4 pp. Written after the première of *Ubu Roi*, thanking Bauër for "discovering and announcing" the play and for the two articles he wrote supporting it.

254. Holograph letter signed from Charles Morin to Henry Bauër [17 December 1896], 3 pp. Written the week after the première, giving Bauër "unpublished details" concerning the authorship of *Ubu Roi*, which he calls the "joint work" of his brother and himself.

255. *Ubu Roi.* Paris: Édition du Mercure de France, 1896. 12mo, full brown mottled calf, inner gilt dentelles, top edges gilt, others uncut.

> First edition. One of the most significant books of the past hundred years, not only for its considerable influence on today's theatre, but also, in a more general sense, as the seedbed of attitudes which have affected the patterns of art and literature increasingly since its publication. Jarry's influence on Picasso, Tzara, Breton, and other major architects of the twentieth century has been enormous.

256. *Ubu Roi ou les polonais. Drame en cinq actes . . . .* The complete play in its original prepublication appearance, in two issues of Paul Fort's short-lived review *Le Livre d'art*, April–May 1896. Bound in one volume, 4to, three-quarter cloth.

257. *Ubu Roi. Drame en cinq actes en prose, restitué en son intégrité tel qu'il a été représenté par les marionnettes du Théâtre des Phynances en 1888 et le Théâtre de l'Oeuvre le 10 décembre 1896, avec la musique de Claude Terrasse.* Paris: Édition du Mercure de France, 1897. 12 mo, three-quarter crushed levant, raised bands, gilt extra, original wrappers bound in, uncut (binding by Canape). One of 10 large-paper copies on China paper (No. 3), of the facsimile edition of the manuscript of Jarry and Terrasse. Signed in ink with the initials "J. T." (Jarry-Terrasse).

258. *Ubu Roi. Avec des lithographies originales et des bois de Edmond Heuzé.* Paris: Marcel Sautier, 1947. 4to, loose in sheets within original illustrated wrappers, uncut, in publisher's slipcase.

> Deluxe edition limited to 200 copies, all on *pur chiffon de Lana.* This is one of a few copies reserved "for the artist and the collaborators," Copy No. VII, printed for J.-G. Daragnès, with an added suite in black and white of the lithographs and a suite in color of eight additional lithographs which were not published.

259. *Répertoire des pantins. Ouverture d'Ubu Roi d'Alfred Jarry pour piano à quatre mains par Claude Terrasse.* [and] *Marche des polonais (extraite d'Ubu Roi, d'Alfred Jarry) pour piano, par Claude Terrasse.* Paris: Édition du Mercure de France, 1898. 2 pieces. Folio. First printing of two of the songs from *Ubu Roi.* The covers are original lithographs by Alfred Jarry.

260. *Ubu sur la butte. Prologue.* Holograph manuscript signed, dated at the end "12 décembre, 1898," 9 pp. Tipped to mounts and bound in one volume, 4to, gilt decorated calf (binding by Dervois fils).

This prologue was written for an abbreviated version of *Ubu Roi* presented in a marionnette theatre at the Cabaret artistique des Quat'zarts on 27 November 1901. The manuscript bears also an earlier title—*Ubu aux 4-z'arts.* The text in its final form was published by Sansot in 1906.

261. 30 holograph postcards signed and a letter written in a minute script on Jarry's carte-de-visite. All are written to the novelist Rachilde and her husband Alfred Vallette, director of the *Mercure de France.* Most of the cards carry views of Jarry's hometown, Laval, in Brittany, and many of them are long letters covering both sides of the card.

In 1894 Jarry had begun to frequent Rachilde's Tuesday salon. (Occasionally he stayed away in order to attend one of Mallarmé's Tuesdays.) In the spring of 1898—along with Rachilde, Vallette, Pierre Quillard, A.-F. Hérold, and Marcel Collière—Jarry rented a villa in Corbeil. By the end of the year he was living there most of the time. He finished the first version of *Par la taille* on 5 December 1898.

The following year, between May and November, he hired a house at La Frette which he used for vacations with Rachilde and Vallette. There he worked on *Ubu Enchaîné* and finished revising *Par la taille* as a libretto for an operetta to be set to music by Claude Terrasse, his collaborator on *Ubu Roi.*

262. *Par la taille. Un acte comique et moral en prose et en vers pour esjouir grands et petits.* Paris: E. Sansot, 1906. 16mo, original wrappers, uncut. First edition. One of 200 copies on *Hollande teinté.*

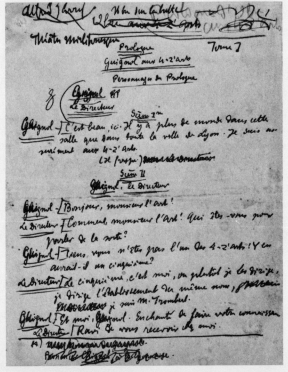

263. *Par la taille*. Holograph manuscript signed, 20 pp. plus title-page. Small 4to. The complete manuscript of the libretto, very different from the published version above.

264. *Par la taille*. Holograph music manuscript signed, by Claude Terrasse, 50 pp. Folio. The complete manuscript, words and music.

265. 9 holograph letters signed from Jarry to Terrasse, 20 pp. Concerning, among other matters, their work on *Par la taille*.

266. *Ubu Enchaîné précédé de Ubu Roi*. Paris: Éditions de la Revue Blanche, 1900. 8vo, contemporary white boards, original wrappers bound in. First edition, inscribed:

> *A Rachilde / ces gros Ubus à pharcir / enchaînés d'un phylet à poissons.*
> *Alfred Jarry.*

Tipped in at the end is an announcement of the forthcoming production of *Ubu Roi* at Lugné-Poe's Théâtre de l'Oeuvre. The announcement is illustrated by a woodcut portrait of Ubu by Jarry.

267. *L'Almanach du Père Ubu, illustré (1899)*. Holograph manuscript and notes, 8 pp. Folio and small 4to. The manuscript index lists material not included in the published version.

268. *Léda. Opérette-bouffe en un acte, par Alfred Jarry et Karl Rosenval* [Berthe Danville]. Holograph manuscript, 46 pp. Small 4to.

Jarry met Berthe Danville in the winter of 1897. In collaboration with her he wrote *Léda* in 1899 and 1900. *Léda* was performed on 15 May 1900, but has not been published.
The manuscript is entirely in Jarry's hand. On the first sheet he has written the title, the cast of characters, and drawn a small sketch of the stage set.

269. *A propos de l'inutilité du théâtre au théâtre* by A.-F. Lugné-Poe. Holograph manuscript signed, 22 pp. 8vo.

In the September 1896 issue of the *Mercure de France*, Jarry had published an article entitled *De l'inutilité du théâtre au théâtre*. In it he called for a simplification of the entire gamut of theatrical production: direction, decor, diction, gesture, and so on. (He was concerned, at that moment, with the production of *Ubu Roi*.)
In this commentary, originally written as a letter from London to Alfred Vallette of the *Mercure*, Lugné-Poe reinforces Jarry's stand, with observations from his experience of French and English theatre.

270. *Alfred Jarry ou le surmâle de lettres. Orné d'un portrait de Cazals* by Rachilde. [Paris] Bernard Grasset (1928). 8vo, original wrappers, uncut. First edition. Review copy.

Scène VIII
LES MÊMES, la Borne s'ouvre; en ait, dans une gloire d'apothéose, L'HOMME ORDINAIRE, en habit noir. Il a les palmes.

CHŒUR FINAL
(L'HOMME ORDINAIRE, tenant la JEUNE FILLE par la taille; LE BOSSU et LE GÉANT, à leur droite et à leur gauche.)

Par la taille {nous nous tenons; LA J. FILLE
               {nous différons; B., G., H. ORD.
Par la taille {il s'empare B., G., J. FILLE
               {je m'empare H. ORD.
Des belles.

(L'HOMME ORDINAIRE et LA JEUNE FILLE disparaissent au fond.)

Scène IX
LE BOSSU et LE GÉANT, dos à dos de chaque côté de la borne.

(On entend sonner une petite pendule.)

LE BOSSU et LE GÉANT
Six heures du soir! Je vais arriver en retard!

(Ils sortent précipitamment, chacun de son côté.)
FIN   Alfred Jarry

263

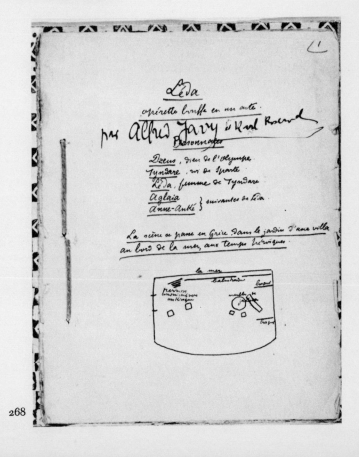

Léda
opérette bouffe en un acte.
par Alfred Jarry et Karl Rosen

Personnages
Zeus, dieu de l'olympe.
Tyndare, roi de Sparte
Léda, femme de Tyndare
Aglaé
Anne-Anté } suivantes de Léda.

La scène se passe en Grèce dans le jardin d'une villa au bord de la mer, aux temps héroïques.

268

271. *De la grandeur.* [Paris] chez Bernard Grasset, 1952. 8vo, original wrappers, uncut. First edition. One of 1,500 numbered copies on *Alfa mousse.*

272. *De la grandeur.* Holograph manuscript, 280 pp. 8vo. The complete manuscript of the book with additional material not published.

273. *De la grandeur.* Set of proofs ("placards") for this book, with many holograph corrections, deletions, and additions.

274. 17 holograph letters signed to Joë Bousquet, 1928–1936. One letter includes a snapshot of Jouhandeau.

JULES LAFORGUE

275. *Le Concile féerique.* Paris: Publications de La Vogue, 1886. 8vo, silk boards, original wrappers bound in, uncut. Daragnès bookplate.

First edition of Laforgue's rarest book, limited to 50 numbered copies. This one is numbered 25 and is signed, with his initials, by the publisher, Gustave Kahn. On the front cover is the ticket of Léon Vanier, Libraire-Editeur.

Tipped in is a two-page holograph manuscript signed by René Ghil, dated October 1886, concerning Jules Laforgue.

276. Holograph manuscript drafts of poems, 6 pp.

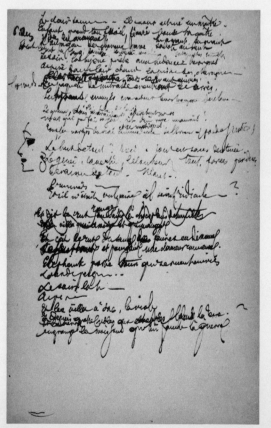

277. *Histoire de Bossuet, évêque de Meaux.* Holograph manuscript, 10 December 1853, 200 pp. 4to, contemporary half-shagreen.

The manuscript of the complete work. Lamartine's pagination jumps from 31 to 33, but nothing is lacking; 48 and 49 are on one sheet; there are two pages numbered 112, resulting in a misplacement by the binder of page 112 (bis) following page 113.

There are many variants from the published text, and many long passages in the manuscript have been deleted. There are a number of corrections throughout, especially in the more important sections, such as in Lamartine's parallel between Bossuet and Fénelon.

The entire manuscript is holograph with the exception of four pages (179–182), which are quotations apparently copied for Lamartine by his wife.

VALERY LARBAUD

278. *Itinéraire (décrit) de mes personnages.* Holograph manuscript, 3 pp. (incomplete).

Larbaud—translator of Joyce, Samuel Butler, Whitman, and many other non-French writers—was a wide-ranging reader, writer, and traveler, and a major force in the deparochializing of twentieth-century French literary taste. This outline of the backgrounds and itineraries of some of his own characters reflects his cosmopolitan spirit.

279. *Remarques pour Maurice Martin du Gard*. Holograph manuscript, 14 pp. Folio.

An autobiographical analysis of Larbaud's life ("private . . . withdrawn") and work (poetry, novels, short stories, essays, translations, criticism).

> . . . My mother. *The sole obstacle* . . . not one intimate friend, a true confidant . . . the real *me* is in my books; action has no place in my life, hence my best friend, the one who knows me best is he who has . . . read my books the most attentively . . . . There are so few *attentive* readers! . . . I never forget that literature is a collective work, like the cathedrals—with this difference, that it is never finished. "One of the French workmen," nothing more nor less. My name engraved, more or less deeply, on the stone.

280. 42 pieces of correspondence addressed to Maurice Martin du Gard, director of the reviews *Les Écrits Nouveaux* and *Les Nouvelles Littéraires*. In one of the letters he draws a map to show Martin du Gard where Joyce is staying.

281. 3 holograph letters signed to Jacques Fourcade, July–October 1930, 8 pp. Concerning royalties due him for the French translation of *Ulysses* published by Fourcade and Adrienne Monnier.

282. 5 photographs of Valery Larbaud, 3 with holograph annotations by him.

LE CORBUSIER

283. *Rome*. Holograph manuscript signed, illustrated with 6 pen-and-ink drawings, 5 pp. Folio, in half-morocco binding. An analysis of Rome as forms in space—"a prodigious poem of geometry and nature."

284. 6 holograph letters signed to his publisher, 17 pp. Concerning his book *Destin de Paris*, with 18 pages of his pencil sketches for the book's illustrations, 29 proofs of the illustrations, and 2 related letters.

285. 2 original lithographs in color, one a trial proof on China paper, 1932–1936.

MICHEL LEIRIS

286. *L'Afrique fantôme*. The complete manuscript, in 7 notebooks, 716 pp. Within 2 morocco-backed slipcases (binding by Mercher).

The first notebook is written in ink; the six others are carbon copies of the original holograph manuscript, the pages bearing the original impression having been removed from the notebooks and subsequently lost. These carbons bear some holograph corrections and additions.

vendredi.

Cher Monsieur,

je suis surpris d'apprendre que Joyce
n'est pas au N° 10 de la rue de l'U-
-niversité; je me suis peut-être trom-
-pé quant au numéro, mais voici
le plan :

Hôtel où habite Joyce.

Portes

rue des saints Pères

rue Jacob

Veuillez agréer, cher Monsieur, mes
sincères salutations.   V. Larbaud.

280

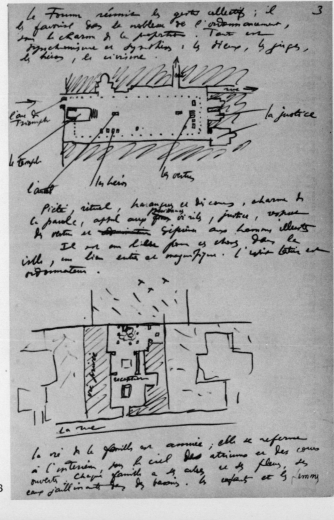

283

3

Brief portions of the text appeared in the first issue of the review *Minotaure*. The book was published originally by Gallimard in 1934. That edition was banned and then destroyed during the Nazi occupation.

Laid in is a handbill announcing the book's publication; on the verso, the following presentation inscription: "Pour André Lefèvre, biblio- et africano-phile, avec toute l'amitié de Michel Leiris. 21-3-54."

An important transitional work on Leiris's route from poetry to confession.

FRANZ LISZT

287. 33 holograph letters signed from Liszt to his daughters Blandine (later Mme. Émile Ollivier) and Cosima (later the wife of Hans von Bülow and, after that, of Wagner), 25 March 1850 to 19 July 1862. 4to and 8vo.

Franz Liszt and the Comtesse d'Agoult had two daughters and a son. At the end of 1839, when Liszt left for Vienna to begin a long series of concert appearances, the girls, aged 4 and 2, were sent to Paris to live with Liszt's mother. In 1844, after the definitive break between Liszt and Mme. d'Agoult, Blandine was sent to the boarding school of Mme. Louise Bernard in Montparnasse. Two years later Cosima followed her there. Liszt was determined, however, to keep a close watch on his daughters' education, and after an unauthorized visit they made to their mother in February 1850, he decided to move them from Mme. Bernard's pension to the more careful supervision of Mme. Patersi de Fossombroni. Mme. Patersi de Fossombroni was the former teacher of Princess Sayn-Wittgenstein, with whom Liszt had been involved since the year before his appointment as Kapellmeister at the Court of Weimar, in 1848.

Liszt saw less and less of Blandine and Cosima in the years ahead, but through his letters he gives evidence of his great concern. He tried to be constantly aware of what they needed beyond their formal instruction, and his letters were designed to help supply those needs. He is often tender, sometimes severe, but always enlightened and enlightening, as concerned with moral questions as with intellectual and artistic ones. He discusses his daughters' reading, their studies, their writing style, and sends them books. He writes often of music, their musical education, his own work and that of Chopin, Wagner, Gounod, and César Franck, among others.

In 1855 the girls visited Liszt at Weimar, stayed the winter in Berlin, then went back to Paris. Cosima returned to Berlin to marry Hans von Bülow, who had been one of Liszt's favorite pupils. Blandine then went to live with her mother in Paris, and at one of her receptions she met Émile Ollivier, a rising young lawyer and politician, with whom she fell in love. Both Liszt and Mme. d'Agoult were pleased with the match and the marriage took place in Florence on 22 October 1857.

After her marriage, Blandine's relations with Liszt were warmer and deeper than ever. They continued their detailed exchange of ideas by letter. Blandine's marriage was idyllic in all respects, but on 11 September 1862, two months after the birth of a son, she died at the age of 26. Liszt's last letter to her is dated 19 July 1862.

288. 117 holograph letters signed from Blandine and Cosima to Liszt during the same period.

289. *Gaudeamus igitur. Humoreske für Soli, Chor und Orchester.* Holograph music manuscript signed, 29 pp. plus title-page. Folio. With a 9-line presentation inscription on the title-page from Liszt to Dr. Gille, of Jena, on the 100th-anniversary Jubilee of the Jena Academic Festival Concerts, 13 January 1870.

Music and text are in Liszt's hand throughout. At the time of inscribing the manuscript to Dr. Gille, Liszt went over the entire composition and made many changes, additions, and annotations.

... [Liszt] is modern not only by virtue of certain discoveries in harmonics, chord structure, etc., but because his perpetual search for the new, unique in nineteenth-century music, has proved to be the cornerstone of modern aesthetics.

Liszt: The Artist as Romantic Hero by Perényi. Boston: Atlantic-Little, Brown, 1974.

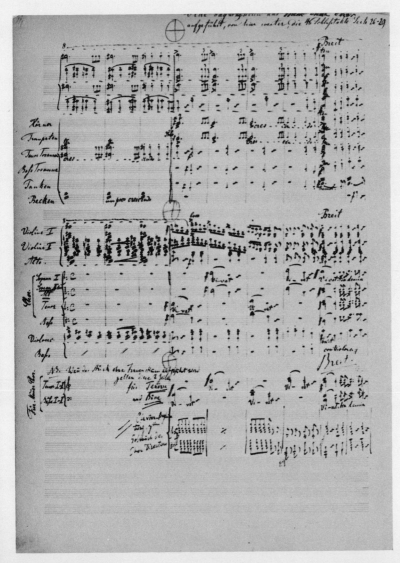

290. *Astarté.* [Paris: Librairie de l'Art Indépendant] 1891. 4to, half-morocco, gilt top, original wrappers bound in. First edition. One of 75 numbered copies on Holland paper. Louÿs's rare first book, published when he was 20.

291. *Astarté.* Several sets of proof sheets of the first edition, bound together with the holograph manuscripts of progressive states of the poems. In some instances as many as 12 variant drafts of a poem are present, making it possible to follow the poem from initial idea to finished state. These manuscripts are bound within the framework of Louÿs's maquette for the volume: drafts of title-page, table of contents, and related material. Some of the manuscripts are signed with his early pseudonym—Claude Moreau. There are 176 manuscript pages relating to *Astarté*, in addition to the proofs; a 5-page manuscript of a ballet, *Daphnis et Chloé*; and a 6-page manuscript concerning Dumas fils. All of these are bound in one volume, 4to, full midnight-blue crushed levant, gilt edges (binding by Gonon).

291

292. Holograph manuscript, 190 pp., drafts and notes for the work which Louÿs hoped to publish on the Corneille-Molière question but never completed. Together with 8 holograph letters signed from Louÿs to the writer Charles Moulié, 1919–1921, 30 pp., relating to Louÿs's research on the project.

Louÿs had worked out a theory that Corneille was responsible for the best in Molière's plays. According to Paul Valéry, who heard him expose his thesis on several occasions:

> . . . there is a conviction, a lucidity, a knowledge of his subject which impresses me. . . . Also a certain irritation and a real anger . . . that people refuse to hear him out, to learn the complete system of proofs before making up their minds about his thesis. . . . What troubles him most is the opinion some have come up with that this is a literary hoax. But this irritation actually sharpens . . . his desire to be right. . . . And so he reads Corneille as no one has ever been able to read him before.

Valéry can vouch only vaguely for the impressive historical documentation Louÿs has drawn up, but "l'artisan en matière de vers" in him is almost completely won over, and he admires the tremendous work Louÿs has done in his analysis of French verse. Valéry concludes:

> . . . I believe he makes of Corneille an author so completely renewed as to appear new. I wouldn't be surprised if, once his entire study is published, there come about, for the art of French verse, important and infinitely desirable results. . . .

293. *Qui l'ignorait?* Holograph manuscript, 32 pp. Small 4to.

In an anonymous article in the press on 18 October 1919, one French critic wrote, ". . . M. Pierre Louÿs ingeniously combines certain dates and certain facts. He demonstrates that Corneille . . . that Molière . . . *Tout cela, qui l'ignorait?* . . ." This manuscript consists of three drafts of Louÿs's answer to his scoffing, anonymous critic. It includes a brilliantly suggestive résumé of how a provincial actor, Molière, became a great playwright in the critical year 1658 as a result of six months' close study of—and with—Corneille, in Rouen. Louÿs also sketches in a piece of ingenious literary detection in the case of Victor Hugo and damns the conventional Sorbonne producers of literary manuals for their lack of insight and imagination.

294. *Pervigilium mortis.* Holograph manuscript, 29 pp. 8vo. Draft versions, with many unpublished passages, of Louÿs's most important poem. Also 11 pages of proofs of the poem and five typewritten versions of it; cuttings of articles about it by Yves-Gérard Le Dantec from *Les Nouvelles Littéraires* and the *Mercure de France*, the second with some corrections.

295. *Pervigilium mortis*. Holograph manuscript, 12 pp. Oblong 8vo. With 12 pages of a worked-over manuscript copy in an unidentified hand, with variants and differing substantially from both published versions. The manuscript copy bears the following note in the hand of Serrière, Louÿs's secretary:

> Très précieux texte du *Pervigilium mortis*. Composé par et sur les indications du maître, novembre 1924–janvier 1925. Je me souviens des longues heures passées avec le maître, ses hésitations et puis son refus catégorique. Défense même d'en parler. Je crois avoir fait un travail identique pour *Poétique*. 1944. G. Serrière.

This manuscript offers a version which differs widely from the two hitherto known, and some of its stanzas are completely unpublished. Le Dantec and other critics considered this work as belonging in the company of such poems as Vigny's *La Maison du berger*, Hugo's *Tristesse d'Olympio*, and Baudelaire's *Le Balcon*.

296. 10 holograph letter drafts and notes to or for Paul Valéry, 22 pp.

The influence of Pierre Louÿs on Valéry during their formative years was determining, and the two friends continued for years to exchange ideas by letter. (Louÿs's influence was similarly significant in the case of Debussy.)

In one of these unfinished drafts, Louÿs rages against Shelley, then soothes himself with reflections on "mon Keats."

Among all the writers of his period, Louÿs had, easily, the keenest critical intelligence in matters of poetry—or of literature in general, as Valéry was the first to proclaim. His career and reputation suffered as a result of an early popular success and its effects in dispersing his energies.

297. Holograph letter signed to the influential critic Paul Souday, 2 pp. Alerts Souday to the forthcoming publication of Valéry's *La Jeune Parque*. Souday's enthusiastic review helped to establish the book as one of the milestones of modern poetry.

298. *Poétique*. Paris: Mercure de France, 1916. 8vo, original wrappers, uncut. First edition, an offprint from the issue of 1 June 1916. Louÿs's statement of his poetic doctrine.

299. *Poétique*. Paris: Crès, 1917. Square 12mo, original wrappers, uncut. First edition in book form. One of 25 numbered copies on *Japon impérial*.

300. 6 holograph letters signed from Natalie Clifford Barney to Pierre Louÿs. Invites him to join a small group of friends at the "Temple of Friendship" to hear Paul Valéry tell how he wrote *La Jeune Parque*, which had just been published. One of the letters is written on the verso of a photograph of the Temple (in her garden, at 20 Rue Jacob, Paris).

301. Photograph of Pierre Louÿs taken in 1896, at the time of the publication of *Aphrodite*.

Puisque j'ai cette occasion de vous écrire, puis-je vous signaler un poëme de toute beauté, que vous recevrez bien tôt ou que je vous enverrais si l'extrême modestie de l'auteur renonçait à en faire service :

— La Jeune Parque, de Paul Valéry.

— Je crois que c'est un chef d'œuvre de notre littérature.

Votre amicalement dévoué

Pierre Louÿs

Pneumatique

Monsieur Paul Souday
9 rue Guénégaud
Paris. 6e

297

5

Où le dur sabot sonne
Un Rythme que personne
Jamais n'ouït avant
Leur pas savant.

Nulle autre apothéose !
Le divin Gautier ose
Dans l'antique verger
Être berger :

Oui ! tant que la verdure
Elyséenne dure
Sur sa tête, j'entends,
Vainqueur des temps,

Non l'éclat que répète
Quelque illustre trompette,
Mais ses chevaux hennir
Dans l'avenir.

John Payne

303

304

306

302. *Le Tombeau de Théophile Gautier*. Paris: Alphonse Lemerre, 1873. Small 4to, three-quarter morocco, raised bands, top edges gilt, original wrappers bound in. First edition.

303. *Ode*. Manuscript signed "John Payne," 5 pp. 8vo.

This 68-line poem, composed in French by John Payne, appeared in *Le Tombeau de Théophile Gautier*, on pages 128–131, preceded on pages 125–127 by another poem signed by Payne—in English—*A Funeral Song for Théophile Gautier*. The manuscript is entirely in the hand of Mallarmé, including the signature. It seems unlikely that it could be a copy; it would appear to be a final draft, since there are five substantive textual changes in Mallarmé's hand.

Immediately after Gautier's death on 23 October 1872, Albert Glatigny had suggested to Théodore de Banville the publication of a volume of poems in tribute to Gautier. Lemerre agreed to publish the book. Contributors included Victor Hugo, Leconte de Lisle, Banville, Anatole France, Charles Cros, and Mallarmé, whose *Toast funèbre*, undoubtedly the most moving poem in the collection of more than eighty, stands as one of his finest works.

Swinburne sent six contributions, including a sonnet and an ode in French. The discovery of this manuscript, unknown to Mondor and other Mallarmé specialists, raises a number of nagging questions. Did Payne, who was a fervent admirer of Swinburne, feel he had to match his master's gesture, yet fear to have his own French version of his poem rejected? There are occasional vague echoes in Payne's *Ode* of some of the poetic ideas and references in his other contribution, but in technique, manner, and quality, the two are poles apart. Payne was on intimate terms with Mallarmé—they never failed to *tutoyer* each other in their letters—and it would be interesting to attempt to determine just what role Mallarmé played in the development of the poem signed (by Mallarmé) with the name of his friend Payne.

304. *L'Après-midi d'un faune. Églogue par Stéphane Mallarmé, avec frontispice, fleurons & cul-de-lampe*. Paris: Alphonse Derenne, 1876. Small folio, full decorated parchment, original Japan-paper heavy wrappers bound in, uncut.

First edition. One of 195 numbered copies, this one (numbered in red ink by Mallarmé) No. 182. The illustrations are by Édouard Manet, and two of them have been tinted in pale pink. This copy belonged to Mallarmé's friend the painter Albert Besnard, who decorated the front cover with an oil painting of a standing female nude (11½" x 7¾"). Bound in between the original Japan paper covers and the parchment binding are two contemporary examples of the *kwacho*, the Japanese wood engravings then newly in vogue in France.

In an essay on Mallarmé and *L'Après-midi d'un faune*, Edmund Gosse wrote, "his aim . . . is to use words in such harmonious combination as will suggest to the reader a mood or a condition *which is not mentioned in the text*, but is nevertheless paramount in the poet's mind at the moment of composition." In answer, Mallarmé wrote to Gosse telling him "your study is a miracle of divination." He cited the passage quoted above, underlining the italicized clause, and added, "It's all there."

305. *L'Après-midi d'un faune. Églogue par Stéphane Mallarmé. Edition définitive.* Paris: La Revue Indépendante, 1882 [1887]. 8vo, cloth-backed boards, original wrappers bound in, uncut. Second edition, on *papier vergé.* Presentation copy, inscribed by Mallarmé to the drama critic Henry Bauër.

Mallarmé published this so-called "definitive edition" to correct the faulty meter in the 46th verse of the original edition.

306. *Vers et prose. Morceaux choisis. Avec un portrait par James M. N. Whistler.* Paris: Perrin et Cie., 1893. 8vo, full brown crushed levant, raised bands, doublures of lighter brown levant, end-leaves of watered silk, top edges gilt, original wrappers bound in, uncut (binding by Yseux, successeur de Thierry-Simier).

First edition. One of 25 numbered large-paper copies on *Hollande van Gelder.* The frontispiece—one of the best portraits, along with Gauguin's, of Mallarmé— is an original lithograph by Whistler. Here, in the large-paper copy, it is present in two states.

Presentation copy, inscribed by Mallarmé to Roger Marx, the most perceptive collector of modern art in France at the end of the nineteenth century, editor-in-chief of *La Gazette des Beaux-Arts,* friend of Gide, Huysmans, Mallarmé, portrayed by Carrière, Rodin, Besnard, and many other artists.

Tipped in are two letters from Mallarmé to Roger Marx (one on his carte-de-visite, the other on his customary correspondence card), with their envelopes, and dating from February 1892. They concern, among other matters, plans for meetings with Whistler.

307. *Un Coup de dés jamais n'abolira le hasard. Poème* [Paris: Éditions de La Nouvelle Revue Française, 1914]. Folio, original wrappers, uncut.

First edition. The poem was published first, tentatively, in the May 1897 issue of the review *Cosmopolis,* and in book form in 1914, 16 years after Mallarmé's death. Its typographical innovations had considerable influence on Apollinaire, Cocteau, and many others. For Mallarmé the typography was an active symbol of his insistence that the poet have greater freedom in his confrontation with time and space: the freedom of the painter before the empty canvas, and of the musician, whose work will become, in Gide's phrase, the animation of a time-frame.

As much as anything Mallarmé wrote, this poem illustrates his ambition, as he put it in a letter to Verlaine, to write "the Orphic explanation of the earth, which is the sole duty of the poet and the literary game par excellence."

308. Holograph letters addressed by Mallarmé to Villiers de l'Isle-Adam, Huysmans, Coppée, Charles Morice, Edmund Gosse, John Payne, York Powell, Édouard Dujardin, Félix Fénéon, Courteline, Henri Cazalis, and Henry Roujon.

309. Holograph letter signed from J. Clément to Mallarmé, Besançon, 16 May 1876, 4 pp., with envelope.

Mallarmé was by profession a secondary-school English teacher. This letter, from the former principal of the lycée in Sens where Mallarmé had been a student, is a friendly warning that government inspectors from the National Education Ministry are planning to turn in an unfavorable fitness report on Mallarmé's teaching, and that as a result he may be transferred from Paris to a post in the provinces.

See also ODILON REDON, no. 373.

ANDRÉ MALRAUX

310. *La Tentation de l'occident.* Paris: Bernard Grasset, 1926. 8vo, original wrappers, uncut. First edition. Inscribed:

A Fernand Fleuret / son ami / A. Malraux / [small ink sketch].

311. *Les Conquérants.* Paris: Bernard Grasset (1928). 8vo, original wrappers, uncut. First edition. Numbered review copy, inscribed:

A Monsieur Émile Vuillermoz / hommage de l'auteur / André Malraux.

312. *Les Puissances du désert. La Voie Royale.* Paris: Éditions Bernard Grasset, 1930. First edition. Numbered review copy, inscribed:

A Émile Vuillermoz / hommage de l'auteur / André Malraux.

313. *La Condition humaine.* Paris: Librairie Gallimard (1933). 8vo, original wrappers, uncut. First edition. One of 209 numbered copies on *vélin pur fil Lafuma Navarre.*

314. *Le Temps du mépris.* Paris: Gallimard [1935]. 8vo, original wrappers, uncut. First edition. Review copy, inscribed:

A Marcel Jouhandeau / avec le sympathique souvenir de / André Malraux.

Jouhandeau, one of the finest (and purest) modern French prose stylists, has made markings in the margins of a number of pages.

315. *L'Espoir. Roman.* Paris: Gallimard (1937). 8vo, three-quarter brown crushed levant, raised bands, gilt top, original wrappers bound in. First edition. One of 230 numbered copies on *Alfa mousse.* Inscribed on half-title:

Pour Jacques Diéterle / bien cordialement / André Malraux / juin 46.

- Qu'est-ce qu'il était? demanda Garcia, comme si, de ~~continuer~~
à parler~~/~~du blessé eût supprimé ~~cette~~ porte refermée sur lui.

- Mécano. Chez Hispano, à Guadalajara. Il était aux milices; ~~il~~
~~avait du sang-froid.~~ Alors on l'a mis dans l'aviation. Bombardier.

- Militant?

- ~~Rensse-tu~~

- Pourquoi était-il avec nous?

- Où que t'aurais voulu qu'il soit, Mécano. Chez les fascistes?

- Non, bien sûr: nulle part.

- Oh! ça...

Barca écarquilla les sourcils, releva la t^ete: la douleur
le reprit. Il reposa la tête sur l'oreiller, et son vieux visage
reprit l'expression de la douleur persistante - les yeux plus
creux, les traits toujours prêts à changer - cette expression
d'une enfance inconnue, à la fois vulnérable et grave, ~~de~~ la
souffrance tire de chaque visage la noblesse qu'il cache.

[handwritten paragraph, partially legible]

Et Sierra Garcia ne vit remarquer...

Comment ça va, au moins dit-il :

*Rien. Quoi. Mais je ne sais pas : je n'y vois plus. On m'a envoyé
aux renseignements militaires.*

C'est pour ? De contre-espionnage ?

Et de problèmes d'organisation.

J'a content ?

J'aime faire ce que je sais faire.

Malgré la porte fermée, ils entendirent de nouveau le cri.

316

317

316. *L'Espoir*. Typescript with holograph corrections and additions, 11 pp. 4to. This is the first chapter of the third section of Part I, *L'Illusion lyrique*, with many variants from the published text. The novel is based on Malraux's experiences during the Spanish Civil War and is dedicated to the comrades who fought with him at Teruel.

HENRI MATISSE

317. 3 linoleum blocks cut by Matisse during the 1930s with a view to illustrating a deluxe edition of Baudelaire's *Les Fleurs du mal*, to be designed and printed by Daragnès. Their plans fell through and the work was never finished.

Seated Woman (*La Tahitienne*). 11⅛" x 7¾".

Head of a Woman, profile. 6½" x 3½".

Head of a Woman, face view. 6½" x 3½".

> I want to say a few words about linoleum engraving. Linoleum should not be chosen as an economical substitute for wood, for it gives the engraving a special character, very different from that of a wood engraving, one for which it should be sought out.
>
> I have often thought that this very simple medium is comparable to the violin with its bow: a surface, an engraving tool—four taut strings and a switch of horsehair. The gouge like the bow is a direct extension of the engraver's sensitivity . . . the slightest distraction during the course of a line brings, involuntarily, a slight pressure from the fingers to the gouge, with an adverse effect on the line. In the same way one has only to tighten a bit the fingers holding the bow in order for the sound to change its character— soft becomes loud.
>
> Linoleum engraving is a true medium predestined for the painter-illustrator.
>
> *Comment j'ai fait mes livres* by Matisse.

318. 20 holograph letters signed from Matisse to Daragnès, 1936–1947, 2 of them with pen-and-ink drawings by Matisse; together with other documents related to their collaboration. In all, 42 pieces.

319. Photograph, by Brassaï, of Matisse drawing.

320. Holograph manuscript notebook, 15 pp. Drafts for stories, considerably rewritten, and with several pen-and-ink sketches.

321. *Paroles en Espagne.* Holograph manuscript and typescript with holograph revisions, 32 pp. ". . . Baudelaire se plaignait un jour de ce qu'en France tout le monde ressemble à Voltaire."

322. *Une Morale politique.* Corrected typescript, 4 pp. The conflict between politics and morality: Mauriac takes issue with Thierry Maulnier.

323. *Hommage à François Mauriac.* Paris: Éditions du Siècle, 1933. 8vo, three-quarter morocco, raised bands, top edges gilt, original wrappers bound in, uncut.

> Special number of *La Revue du Siècle* (July-August 1933), with tributes to Mauriac by Cocteau, Drieu la Rochelle, Duhamel, Lacretelle, Roger Martin du Gard, Maurois, Montherlant, Paul Morand, and others.
>
> Bound in are the publisher's mimeographed *Schéma du Numéro Mauriac*, the menu of the dinner honoring Mauriac on 14 December 1933, and holograph letters relating to this publication by Irène Nemirovsky, Jean Paulhan, Marcel Aymé, Paul Claudel, Paul Morand, Emmanuel Berl, Philippe Hériat, Jean Guéhenno, Jean Schlumberger, Robert Vallery-Radot, and others.

HENRI MICHAUX

324. *Entre centre et absence.* Paris: H. Matarasso [1936]. With 7 drawings and a frontispiece by the author. Square 12mo, original wrappers, uncut.

> First edition of the first book written and illustrated by Michaux. One of 300 numbered copies on *papier vélin.* With the following inscription on the limitation page:
>
> > A Mouny de Boully (Pascal / de bonne mémoire) / Hommage très amical de l'éditeur. / H. Matarasso.
>
> Laid in is the complete typescript of the book typed by Michaux, 24 pp., with holograph corrections (including one corrected tear sheet). Mostly folio. In addition there is a manuscript title-page in Michaux's hand, with the following note by the publisher: "Seul manuscrit (dactylographié avec corrections) existant de cet ouvrage de H. Michaux. L'Éditeur, H. M."
>
> Also laid in is the holograph manuscript, in pencil, of the first draft of the poem *Vision*, signed by Michaux with his initials. The poem appears in very different form on pages 33–34 of the book.

325. *Quelques faits personnels.* Typescript with holograph corrections, 8 pp. Michaux drafts much of his writing directly on the typewriter.

326. *Affaires impersonnelles.* Typescript with holograph corrections, 2 pp.

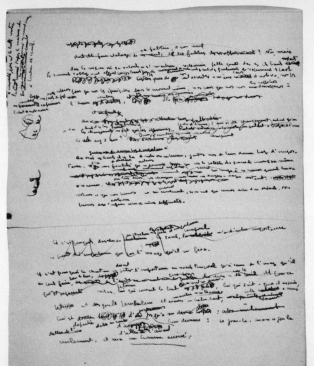

3

Cependant un nouveau soir étant arrivé, un grand engorgement d'îles ~~ne je~~ accumulai secrétement ~~en mon~~ ~~clos~~, crève dans un immense frémissement. Il y a une minute de bascule, une minute de profond renverse-malheur, et la nuit s'achève dans un gouffre d'oubli.

C'est alors que se trace un peu plus profond, le petit sillon , ~~un~~ *cette fois encore* ~~~~, chaque fois, un peu plus profond.

§

Elle repose, sa grande langue soigneusement enclose en sa bouche *sur lèvres imp* ~~~~ entra-ouverte, ⌐ sa grande et succulente langue, pratiquement invisible.

Ils sont cinq autour, avides. Ils attendent. ~~~~

~~et~~ Dès qu'elle ouvrira la bouche, eux aussitôt la maint ~~~~ ouverte, *fonceront* à la recherche de la langue, facile exploration en cette ~~~~ demeure où il n'y a ~~~~ *qu'elle* *grass de* *La fatiguée ; la reposante,* des heures dur ont quelque fois aliment, ~~~~ ~~~~ ~~~~ tant qu'elle peut résiste à l'envie de boire, de bailler, de soupirer, *à voir leur mine allumée* ~~~~ ~~se~~ doutant bien ~~~~ *pour elle s'isole* ~~~~ qui, entre cinq se relayant, se distrayant *les uns les autres* pouvait se surveiller sans cesse? Tôt ou tard, elle s'oublie. Elle entrou *aussitôt* la bouche, ~~~~ de se précipiter, de maintenir ouvert l'imprudent *Malheur. Malheur à qui se* ~~~~ orifice, où la succulente langue ne va pas pouvoir plus arrière *la mordent* se retirer. Ils l'ont . Ils l'ont saisie. Ils la tiennent, ~~~~ grignote

L'horrible repas commence. ⌐

Ils sont cinq. Je suis l'un d'eux.

... le mot ... un peu profane ... semblait ... le tambour major rappeler le tambour major de cette musique ... Les personnes qui ont étudié les rites des temples égyptiens et les ... dessins qui s'y rapportent n'ont pas besoin ... qu'on leur apprenne ... pour se souvenir que ... il s'agissait ... d'une représentation plus solennelle, à la place du ... qui tient le titre, il y a ... le chien sacré, c'est-à-dire Anubis, l'inséparable compagnon et serviteur des deux grands Dieux, dont un membre éminent du clergé symbolisait le rôle au moyen d'une tête de chien, ... Il est presqu'impossible de se livrer à un examen attentif de ce tableau sans en retirer la conviction que ... dans la représentation de ces trois figures, ... où les deux ministres occupent leur place à quelques pas en arrière, la distinction de rang est soigneusement observée.

Le prêtre qui chantait les hymnes et les prières, ou préchantre, jouissait d'une estime particulière. ... qui, sur le degré inférieur du temple, au milieu de la double rangée de peuple, dirigeait au moyen ... d'un bâton en forme de sceptre ... les grecs nommaient ce liturge ou maître ... Chapelle du culte d'Isis le chanteur ou le chanteur d'hymnes (Odos, hymnodos). Il rappelle les rhabdodes et rhapsodes qui chantaient un bâton de laurier à la main, ... au-dessus de l'autel, ... également une sorte de sceptre dans la main, représentant sans doute aussi un chanteur, ou autrement remplit les fonctions analogues à cet office et qu'il est ... d'en distinguer. ...

327

328

327. *Isis* [*Les Filles du feu*]. Holograph manuscript, 6 pp. 4to.

This text first appeared as *Isis. Souvenirs de Pompéi* in *La Phalange* (1845). It was reprinted as *L'Iseum* in *L'Artiste* (1847) and was included, under the title *Isis*, in the volume *Les Filles du feu* in 1854.

Nerval's original point of departure for this text was a paper entitled *Die Isis Vesper* by Karl August Böttiger, German archaeologist and friend of Goethe and Schiller.

The manuscript is extensively corrected, with a number of variants and about forty lines which were omitted from the published version. The six sheets of this manuscript are completed by three additional pages in the collections of the Bibliothèque Spoelberch de Lovenjoul at Chantilly.

Nerval's manuscripts are among the rarest in nineteenth-century French literature. This one, considered for many years as lost, was discovered only recently in an American collection in France.

CLÉMENT PANSAERS

328. *Point d'orgue / programmatique / pour jeune orang-outang*. Holograph manuscript signed, calligraphed in two colors, 80 pp. 16mo. The text is illustrated with an original gouache by Pansaers. The page preceding the gouache bears the imprint, in green, of his right-hand middle finger, so described and signed (initials). The limitation page reads: "cette manuscrite édition génétique / est restreinte à 2 exemplaires / dont celui-ci / No. 01 / à ma tendre marquise / Bianca da Pansa / le 20 mars 1921 / C. Pansaers."

The second (variant) copy of the manuscript is in the Bibliothèque Littéraire Jacques Doucet, Paris.

Accompanying the manuscript is an original photograph signed by Man Ray, which was to have served as frontispiece for a facsimile edition of this Dada text, planned but never produced.

Pansaers, a Belgian writer and artist much influenced by Taoist philosophy, was a brilliant, somewhat solitary member of the Dada movement. In five years of activity he edited a little magazine, *Résurrection*, published five books including *Bar Nicanor* and *Le Pan-pan au cul du nu nègre*, and several other scattered texts, and produced a few woodcuts and small sculptures. Toward the end of his career he worked in Paris for a year, then returned, in October 1922, to Brussels, where he died at the age of 37.

329. *La Vie à Paris*. Holograph manuscript signed [1921], 11 pp. 8vo. An account of the Paris literary season. The opening section is devoted to Alfred Jarry and the reprinting of *Ubu Roi*. Pansaers writes also of Jarry's novels— *Le Surmâle, Messaline*, and *Gestes et opinions du docteur Faustroll, pataphysicien*. For "profound erudition," he can think of only three writers in Jarry's class: Pierre Louÿs, Richard Wagner, and "perhaps Joseph Bédier."

330. *Aseptique noyade pour amateurs programmatiques.* Holograph manuscript signed, 4 pp. 4to.

331. *Marche funèbre.* Holograph manuscript signed, 2 pp. 4to.

332. 41 holograph letters signed to the editor of the Belgian avant-garde review *Ça Ira.* Together with 26 carbon copies of the replies and related documents.

> Pansaers works feverishly but often ineffectually. He sends news of Dada activities in Brussels and Paris, of Picabia, Ezra Pound, Joyce, Cocteau, Auric and the other members of *Les Six,* Breton (who turns against him), Aragon ("my best friend"), Theo van Doesburg, Pierre Reverdy and—his staunch supporter— the open-minded, generous-spirited Valery Larbaud.
>
> Pansaers is constantly preoccupied with his efforts to publish *Point d'orgue.* There are detailed plans for issuing both regular and deluxe editions of the work. As negotiations drag on, Pansaers's health deteriorates, and on 18 October 1921, he writes, "This is all I can undertake for the moment. As far as I am concerned, then, the edition of *Point d'orgue* must wait."

333. Holograph letter signed to Pierre Albert-Birot, 10 February 1921. Written on the verso of a broadside and subscription form for his *Bar Nicanor,* concerning Tzara and plans for a Dada manifestation in Brussels.

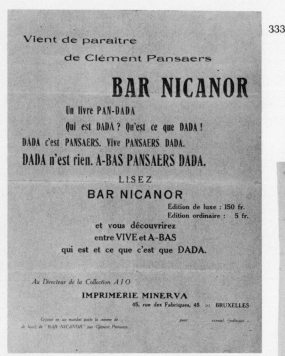

333

334. *Portrait de Pierre MacOrlan.* Original copperplate (steel-faced) engraved by Pascin. Measures 5⅜″ x 3¾″.

335. *Portrait de Pierre MacOrlan.* Original copperplate (steel-faced). Another version, this one unfinished. Measures 5⅜″ x 3⅜″.

336. *Portrait de Tristan Derème.* Original copperplate engraved by Pascin. Measures 4½″ x 3¾″.

337. *Trois filles.* Original etching, Pascin's first, done in the atelier of Daragnès and under his guidance. Composition measures 5⅛″ x 7⅛″. Inscribed in pencil by Pascin, in the right-hand margin:

> à Daragnès, l'élève Pascin.

338. *Rien que la terre à l'exposition coloniale* by Paul Morand. Bound dossier relating to a book designed by Maurice Darantière but never published. The book was to have been illustrated with six watercolors by Pascin (reproduced by the pochoir process) in an edition of 200 copies. The dossier includes whatever records of the project remain:

* Proofs of the text corrected and signed by Paul Morand and with his *bon à tirer*.
* Darantière's maquette for the edition, with 10 sketches of the illustrations tipped in at the appropriate spots.
* Corrected proofs of the text in an earlier (magazine) appearance.
* 18 trial proofs of the illustrations including one colored by hand.
* One large envelope cover addressed by Pascin to Darantière.
* 2 letters from Morand to Darantière.
* 5 letters from Lucy Krohg (Pascin's mistress) to Darantière.
* 3 letter-copies from Darantière to Morand and Lucy Krohg.
* 14 letters and other documents concerning costs and production.

339. *Abécédaire des filles et de l'enfant chéri* [by Pierre MacOrlan]. [Paris] Éditions de la Fanfare de Montparnasse, 1924. With pen-and-ink illustrations, on tinted backgrounds, by Pascin. 16mo, original wrappers, uncut.

Edition limited to 200 copies plus a few copies for the collaborators. This one printed for J.-G. Daragnès. With a presentation inscription signed by Mac-Orlan and Pascin. Daragnès bookplate.

340. *3 petites filles dans la rue. Texte par André Warnod. Dessins en couleurs de Pascin.* [Paris] Éditions de la Fanfare de Montparnasse, 1925. 4to, original wrappers, uncut.

One of 650 numbered copies on *vélin blanc*. Laid in is a proof, in sepia, of the final illustration, with a presentation inscription to Daragnès signed by Warnod and Pascin. Daragnès bookplate.

341. *Aux Lumières de Paris. Illustrations [en couleurs] de Pascin* by Pierre MacOrlan. Paris: Les Éditions G. Crès, 1925. 8vo, original wrappers uncut, in cloth slipcase. One of 1,085 numbered copies on *vélin blanc pur chiffon de Rives*. Daragnès bookplate. Inscribed:

> A Gabriel Daragnès / coeur loyal, avec toute l'affection du vieux Mac. / P. Mac Orlan / .25.

JEAN PAULHAN

342. *Jacob Cow le pirate, ou Si les mots sont des signes.* Paris: Au Sans Pareil, 1921. 16mo, original wrappers, uncut. First edition. One of 500 numbered copies on *vélin Lafuma.* The book is dedicated to Paul Valéry. Erratum slip laid in.

343. *Jacob Cow le pirate* . . . . Holograph manuscript, 31 pp. 4to, in folder lettered by Paulhan. Together with complete sets of corrected galley and page proofs. Laid in is a holograph letter signed from Paulhan to the publisher concerning the book, and Paul Éluard, Max Ernst, and Ribemont-Dessaignes.

344. 72 holograph letters signed to the poet Joë Bousquet, and 10 related documents. Totaling more than 200 pp. A rich literary correspondence covering the years 1931–1947. Paulhan, friend of painters and editor at the *Nouvelle Revue Française* of many of the best writers, sends Bousquet news and gossip of the Paris art and literary world. He writes about Valéry, Aragon, Artaud, Leiris, Éluard, Arland, Frénaud, Péret, Gide, Michaux, Sartre, Léautaud, Malraux, Ponge, and Breton; Fautrier, Dubuffet, Wols, Chagall, Picasso, Braque, Marie Laurencin, and Max Ernst. He discusses in some detail his own work, notably *F. F. ou le critique* and *Les Fleurs de Tarbes.*

PABLO PICASSO

345. *Ex-libris pour Guillaume Apollinaire.* Watercolor and pen-and-ink, 1905. Measures 7 5/8″ x 4 13/16″. Signed, lower right, "Picasso F E C I T." (Zervos I, 225.)

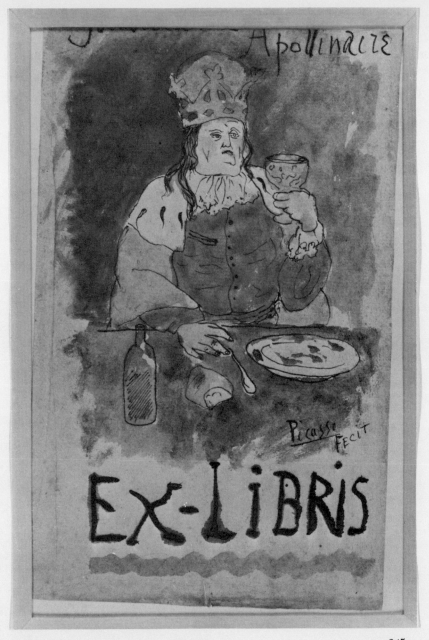

345

Apollinaire met Picasso early in 1905. Moved by Picasso's paintings—"full of pity"—of harlequins and other circus folk, he published an article about him in the May issue of *La Plume*. Soon after that, Picasso sketched this bookplate design for his most bookish friend: ingenious literary journalist, unshy pornographer, perennially frustrated lover, compulsive frequenter of libraries, and incorrigible *lussurioso*, predestined for the Second Circle of Hell—and still the century's greatest lyric poet.

346. *Fernande.* Pen-and-ink sketch signed, ca. 1905. Sheet size, 7″ x 4½″. Drawn on the half-title of *Les Vingt-et-un jours d'un neurasthénique* by Octave Mirbeau (Paris: Fasquelle, 1901).

Fernande Olivier, Picasso's first mistress, with whom he lived during the lean years at the Bateau-Lavoir, is shown in left profile, her long hair trailing down her back.

> . . . Fernande was the first wife of a genius I sat with and she was not the least amusing . . . . Fernande had two subjects hats and perfumes. The first day we talked hats. She liked hats, she had the true french feeling about a hat, if a hat did not provoke some witticism from a man on the street the hat was not a success. Later on once in Montmartre she and I were walking together. She had on a large yellow hat and I had on a much smaller blue one. As we were walking along a workman stopped and called out, there go the sun and the moon shining together. Ah, said Fernande to me with a radiant smile, you see our hats are a success.[4]

> *The Autobiography of Alice B. Toklas* by Gertrude Stein. New York: Harcourt, Brace and Company [1933].

346

[4] In 1952, Fernande Olivier told the author of this catalogue that the "sun and moon" anecdote was pure invention on Gertrude Stein's part. Similar comments concerning the authenticity of other parts of the *Autobiography* have been made by a number of others who participated in the events the book describes—Leo Stein, Matisse, Braque, Tzara, and André Salmon, for example.

Fernande left Picasso in 1912. In 1933 she published *Picasso et ses amis,* her reminiscences of their life together during the "heroic period" at the Bateau-Lavoir, and of their friends Max Jacob, Juan Gris, Apollinaire, Marie Laurencin, Derain, André Salmon, Matisse, Gertrude and Leo Stein, Braque, Vlaminck, van Dongen, the Douanier Rousseau, and all the band.

347. *Hommage à Basket.* Collage-object, fashioned by Picasso for Gertrude Stein, ca. 1928. Measures 5⅞" x 6⅝". White wool over steel-wire supports, satin bow, pink-wool roses in a white-lace basket, mounted on cardboard with a carte-de-visite and holograph inscription by Paul Picasso, in an antique-gilded wooden frame under glass.

In *The Autobiography of Alice B. Toklas,* Gertrude Stein wrote that "Gertrude Stein always says that she only has two real distractions, pictures and automobiles. Perhaps she might now add dogs." Not uncharacteristically, then, in the spring of 1928, she bought herself a white poodle and a new Ford. The poodle she named Basket because Alice Toklas said, "he should carry a basket of flowers in his mouth. Which he never did." The Ford, for a change, she left unnamed.

Over the next ten years Basket became—after Alice Toklas, of course—the most important single figure in Gertrude Stein's life. She and Basket were a familiar sight in the evenings, not only around the Luxembourg and other Left

PAUL PICASSO

voici un petit frère pour votre chien.

La jaca que montaba el picador el domingo de toros en la plaza de ? Mondragon (provincia de Acahuetes) tenía la barriga llena de lirios de azucena ~~y~~ y garbanzos tostados. El picador ~~Angelito~~ Ricardo (el alfileres) puso su pica y firmó en el ~~...~~ gran libro su sentencia.

Cabritos de Lucero ~~...~~ estuvo al quite y se llevó el toro de rodillas y bajo del mortadero. Los sombreros de ostia llovieron como moscas en la ~~partir~~ donde ardía el aceite y la Trini de descaró a donde la tortilla de su vergüenza tirando tiros y dando el retorcido o dondel ~~...~~ ni la poca vergüenza del Lucero ~~...~~ ni el peso del abanico de la capa que barria la nieve no tuvieron que enseñar el trigo y la era sobre el mantel de terciopelo azul lleno de estrellas.

El ~~...~~ de la sed del botijo viñó su carne en el vientre y las pulgas del escaparate estallaron sus migajas en el cañón de la escopeta de los ales.

El trozo de cristal mojado en vino hizo su reverencia y anunció el mantel a puñetazos.

ni la hija ni el novio pudieron estallar una delicia mas y si el cura cantando y bailando su misa mojad por todos el vino del vaso en la salsa y migó el candil en las nubes la rapidez del brazo a migajas limpio untó de mantera ~~...~~ la copa caída mojado por la lluvia ni un solo de perdices pasar el trigo mojado de lentejas de gritos al punta de los perchelas ~~...~~ de jaletes el de oro embarró la seda la espada y clavó los tachuelos al clavo colgado a los correas de la mantilla de ojalata hecho trozos en el suelo y se parió el mismo Revuelto mil en las sábanas mojadas y el peso de ple que que banderillas de fuego lo pusieron de cascabeles las matillas negras del entierro empezaron a repicar las campanas y hacer frio en el pago.

Bank haunts within reasonable range of the Stein pavilion in the Rue de Fleurus, but even farther afield as they wandered "up one street and down another . . . it does feel like any Paris used to . . . and I like to wander with Basket all about it." And she always claimed that listening to the rhythm of Basket drinking water helped her "to recognise the difference between sentences and paragraphs, that paragraphs are emotional and that sentences are not."

Some of her friends thought Basket should have the benefit of constant canine companionship and several of them offered other dogs to serve as a foil to the elegant poodle. Picabia gave her "a tiny Mexican dog," which she named Byron. It remained for Picasso, however, to make the one truly original contribution.

Picasso was then married to the Russian ballerina Olga Khoklova. They had one child, a son Paul, whom everyone called Paulo and who had been born in 1921 on the 4th of February—the day after Gertrude Stein's birthday. It was for Paulo that Gertrude wrote "A Birthday Book" in 1924. It was to have been illustrated by Picasso but was never published.

When Gertrude introduced Basket to Picasso and told him some of her friends disapproved of Basket's growing up an only child, he found his own solution to the problem. He produced a miniature version of Basket, fashioned of white wool over thin steel-wire supports and trimmed fore and aft to correspond to Basket's pattern of clipping. He attached to it a pale tea-rose satin bow. Remembering the reason why the dog had been named Basket, Picasso decided that this Basket should live up to its name and so he placed a bouquet of green-stemmed pink-wool roses in a ruffled white-lace basket and arranged it to hang down from the woolen dog's mouth to between its forepaws. He had a junior-size carte-de-visite imprinted with the name of his son, Paul Picasso, drew three faint parallel pencil lines under the name to serve as a guide for Paulo's seven-year-old hand, and then had Paulo write in ink, between the lines, "Voici un petit frère pour votre chien." He pasted down the card at the center of the bottom of the card-board box, about an inch deep, and attached the miniature Basket and bouquet just above it. The composition was covered with glass, and the box fitted into an antique gilded frame which was sealed up and reinforced at the back with heavy paper painted brown.

348. *Paris le 5 mai 53 I* [and] *Paris le 5 mai 53 II*. 2 holograph manuscript poems in Spanish, 2 pp. Folio.

During the 1930s Picasso began writing poetry. In an article *Picasso poète*, published in *Picasso 1930–1935* (Paris: Cahiers d'Art, 1936), André Breton spoke of "this poetry of a kind that did not exist before," and saw it as another facet of Picasso's painting:

Set against the plastic work, of which it is actually an extension, . . . it is a revolution in the manner of seeing . . . . One understands in this way the need for total expression which takes possession of him and forces him to make up, in that fashion, for the relative inadequacy of one art with respect to the other. One understands just how these two processes, at first sight so separate, can complement each other and, in the end, be made one: this poetry cannot fail to be painterly to the same extent that this painting is poetic . . . .

349

Gertrude Stein, in *Everybody's Autobiography* (New York: Random House, 1937), took a different point of view:

When [Picasso] got rid of his wife he stopped painting and took to writing poetry . . .

He told me about this poetry I had already heard about it, he said he was not going to paint any more perhaps never, he was going to write poetry would I come some evening and listen. I said I would yes and I said I would bring some one who was here now, and I brought along Thornton Wilder . . . .

When I first heard that he was writing poetry I had a funny feeling . . . . Things belong to you and writing belonged to me, there is no doubt about it writing belonged to me . . . .

And so I went over and we all went over Alice B. Toklas and Thornton Wilder . . . to listen all evening to Pablo Picasso's poetry . . . .

The poems were in French and Spanish and first he read a French one and then a Spanish one that he turned into French and then he read on and on and then he looked at me and I drew a long breath and I said it is very interesting . . . . Pablo went on reading . . . and then after a little while we said good night and left. I had a funny feeling the miracle had not come the poetry was not poetry it was well Thornton said like the school of Jean Cocteau and I said for heaven's sake do not tell him. And then I said but after all why should it not be he never felt anything in words and he never read anything unless it was written by a friend and after all he had been brought up in the school of Apollinaire and later Jean Cocteau well of course there was Max [Jacob] . . . .

And a few days after he came over . . . and I did not say anything about his writing. That American he said the one that came he looks interesting what did he say about my writing. He said it was interesting. Yes but did he not say anything more, yes I said he said that certain descriptions that you make have the same quality as your painting. Oh yes said Picasso and he did find it interesting. Yes I said . . . . And you Gertrude he said you do not say much of anything. Well you see Pablo I said you see the egotism of a painter is an entirely different egotism than the egotism of a writer. What do you mean he said well I said I will read you my lecture on painting so I translated it to him, that is very interesting he said. I said well go on writing. Yes he said that is what I am doing. I will never paint again very likely not I like the life of a literary man, I go to cafes and I think and I make poetry and I like it. It is most interesting I said and then for a little time we did not see each other again.

349. *La Vénus du Gaz.* Found object. Height, 10″. A cast-iron burner from a certain type of pre-war French gas stove. When Picasso saw it, he was so struck by its resemblance to his own work that he called it a Picasso "readymade" and christened it *La Vénus du Gaz*:

In three or four thousand years they'll say, perhaps, that at our period, people worshiped Venus in that form, just the way we so confidently catalog old Egyptian things and say, "Oh, it was a cult object, a ritual object used for libations to the gods."

Life with Picasso by Gilot and Lake. New York/Toronto/London: McGraw-Hill Book Company, (1964), page 322.

350. *Picasso et ses amis* by Fernande Olivier. Paris: Librairie Stock, 1933. 12mo, original wrappers, uncut.

Presentation copy. Laid in is a pencil sketch by Fernande Olivier, which she drew to illustrate the extent to which Guillaume Apollinaire's head resembled a pear. Picasso, too, has drawn sketches of Apollinaire emphasizing this feature (see also GUILLAUME APOLLINAIRE, no. 15).

351. Photographs, mostly unpublished, showing Picasso with friends and family at several periods of his life.

MARCEL PROUST

352. Holograph manuscript signed "Marcel P.", ca. September 1893, 4 pp. 12mo. An elaborate tribute to the charms of a friend, Mlle. Germaine Giraudeau, written in her autograph album. There is much in this manuscript to suggest certain passages Proust later incorporated in *Les Plaisirs et les jours* (1896).

353. *A l'ombre des jeunes filles en fleurs*. Paris: Éditions de la Nouvelle Revue Française, 1920. 2 volumes, folio, loose in sheets, within original hand-decorated floral board case, with pink and black silk ties, as issued.

Deluxe edition conceived and designed by Proust himself, and limited to 50 numbered copies on India Bible paper. The frontispiece reproduces the portrait of Proust by Jacques-Émile Blanche. This copy belonged to Robert de Billy, one of Proust's closest friends, and bears his bookplate.

Most of the manuscripts and corrected proof of *A la recherche du temps perdu* are in the Bibliothèque Nationale. The one exception is Proust's manuscript of *A l'ombre des jeunes filles en fleurs*. That manuscript is made up of holograph fragments of widely varying lengths and shapes, of proofs of an unpublished edition (set up by Grasset in 1914), and of those portions of the work which appeared in the June 1914 issue of *La Nouvelle Revue Française*. This whole picturesque and often confusing mass, pasted onto large sheets of heavy paper and folded twice, was divided among the fifty copies of the India Bible paper edition of 1920. Some copies have one of the large folding sheets, others two and, very occasionally, three. The present copy has five: three of them are entirely holograph, and two are corrected proofs with holograph additions.

These sheets show the extent to which the correcting of proof was for Proust simply another phase of rewriting his work.

354. *La Bible d'Amiens. Traduction, notes et préface par Marcel Proust.* [and] *Sésame et les lys. Traduction, notes et préface par Marcel Proust.* Both by John Ruskin. Paris: Mercure de France, 1904–1906. 8vo, contemporary cloth, original wrappers bound in.

353

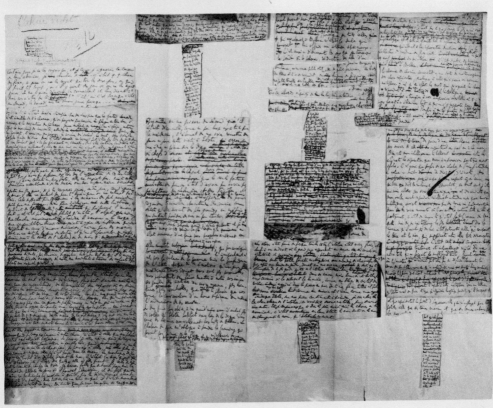

Duranchelle

"Écrire comme on parle" est encore un lieu-commun devant
lequel je m'incline. A condition d'admettre que le style n'étant pas
la parole, il ne s'agit pas d'écrire comme on parle. Mais un grand
écrivain se trouve machiné de telle sorte qu'il pousse en rythme
auquel il n'échappe son aucune des formes de son individu.
[La courbe écrite à l'encre par le baromètre ne ressemble pas
à l'orage mais elle en est le signe. Bien des courbes de style
nous émeuvent, sans que nous le sachions, parcequ'elles sont le
signe d'une voix.

[La voix de Marcel Proust est inoubliable.
[Il m'est difficile de lire son œuvre au lieu de
l'entendre. Parque toujours sa voix s'impose,
et c'est à travers elle que je regarde les mots.

[La prose est une manière d'exprimer
coûte que coûte la pensée. Le reste est
style décoratif. admirer la pensée
de Proust et blâmer son style serait
absurde. Personne au monde ne
fait mieux obéir l'écriture. Personne
au monde ne faisait mieux
obéir la voix. L'une et l'autre

355

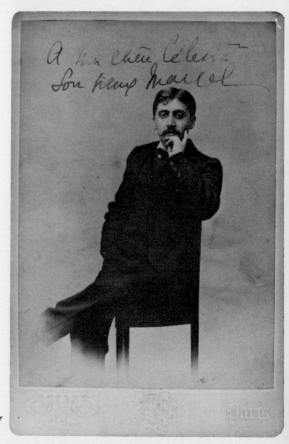

A ma chère Céleste
Son ami Marcel

357

~~xxxxx~~

~~xxxxx~~

~~xxxxx xxxxx xxxxx xxxxx~~

~~xxxxx~~

~~xxxx xxxx xx xxxx xxx~~ ....

M. Pélican
(qui ne sait pas plus nager que toi)

Hortense est une patineuse énergte. Et lorsque la
Seine est gelée, c'est la coutume de transformer le concours
de natation en une épreuve de patinage.

Anselme

En tout cas, c'est grâce à moi qu'Hortense est
célèbre. Je ~~xxxxx~~ ~~xxxxx~~ sa prime pour le professeur
de photographie. Voulant être fixée sur le degré
d'amour ~~xxxxx~~ de M. Chantecler elle avait demandé
au petit Noël le lui offrir un bouquet de
marguerite. Et c'est moi qui, pour faire une farce
à Hortense, ai arraché un pétale à chaque
marguerite

~~xxxx~~
M. et Mme Pélican (ensemble)

Quel poète !

Scène VII
~~M. Pélican, Mme Pélican, Anselme, plus M. Chantecler
et Hortense
(qu'il n'entend pas
le noir)~~

~~xxxxx~~ Hortense (à M. Pélican)
~~xxxxx xxxxx xxxxx xxxxx~~
~~xxxxx xxxxx xxxxx xx fille~~ Papa, est-ce que
je peux épouser M. Chantecler ?

M. Pélican
Fais ce que bon te semble, mon enfant, quoique, maintenant, tu puisses prétendre à un parti plus

358

First editions of Proust's translations of Ruskin, inscribed by Proust to Robert de La Sizeranne, author of *Ruskin et la religion de la beauté* (1897). Each volume has penciled marginal markings and annotations by La Sizeranne.

The books are accompanied by six holograph letters and two holograph postcards, signed, totaling 23 sides. Proust discusses with La Sizeranne some of the nuances of Ruskin's text as well as the delicate situation in which he finds himself as a result of having agreed to edit a selection of Ruskin's writings for the *Mercure de France* and then learning that La Sizeranne, the preeminent French Ruskin scholar of the day, has been working for some time on a similar project. Obviously embarrassed—indeed, almost anguished—in view of La Sizeranne's greater competence for the job, Proust, painstakingly and with excessive tact, manages to find a happy solution for the potential conflict.

355. *La Voix de Marcel Proust* by Jean Cocteau. Holograph manuscript signed, 8 pp. With covering holograph letter signed. "The voice of Marcel Proust is unforgettable. It is difficult for me to *read* his work instead of hearing it. . . . That voice didn't come from the throat, but from the center of his being. . . ."

356. *Alfred Stevens* by Comte Robert de Montesquiou. An offprint from *La Gazette des Beaux-Arts* of an illustrated monograph concerning the Belgian painter Alfred Stevens, by the poet and society figure who served as Proust's principal model for the character Baron de Charlus. Presentation copy, inscribed by the author:

A Marcel Proust / cette critique crinoline. / R. M.

357. 2 photographs of Proust by Otto. 1 cabinet size, 1 carte-de-visite. Inscribed by Proust to his devoted servant, Céleste Albaret:

A ma chère Céleste / son vieux Marcel [and] A Céleste, tendre / et reconnaissant / souvenir du tyran / détesté. / Marcel Proust.

A third photograph, also by Otto, is of Proust's mother.

RAYMOND RADIGUET

358. *Les Pélican.* Holograph manuscript, dated "Paris—St. Maur, Novembre 1919," 20 pp. Folio, in a decorative binding of Japanese boards framed within dark-green calf borders and backstrip (binding by Alix).

This play in two acts, a precursor of the Theatre of the Absurd, was first produced on 24 May 1921, and is Radiguet's only play. The manuscript contains passages omitted from the printed text, including several that are necessary for a full understanding of action and dialogue.

359. *Les Pélican.* Prospectus for the first edition. Penciled note in Valentine Hugo's hand.

360. Holograph poems, 17 pp.; corrected typescript, 4 pp.; and corrected proofs of poems, 10 pp. In board folder inscribed, in Radiguet's hand:

Poèmes inédits / Devoirs de vacances / Les Joues en feu.

361. *Institut de beauté* [and] *Carnaval.* Holograph manuscript of 2 poems.

362. 3 pen-and-ink drawings. 10⅜″ x 8¼″ (2) and 5¼″ x 8¼″. One is inscribed by Radiguet:

à mon sympathique / confrère V. Hugo / A. de Lamartine.

These drawings were given by Radiguet to Valentine Hugo. By referring to her, in his inscription, as V. Hugo, Radiguet conjures up the image of another V. Hugo—Victor Hugo—and signs, facetiously, with the name of Victor Hugo's fellow-Romantic, Alphonse de Lamartine.

363. *Devoirs de vacances. Images d'Irène Lagut.* Paris: A La Sirène, 1921. Small 4to, decorated boards, original wrappers bound in.

First edition. One of 150 numbered copies on *papier vergé.* Tipped in are: a contemporary photograph of Radiguet and Jean Cocteau; the original manuscript of a poem, *L'Examen,* by Radiguet; a holograph music manuscript, *Alphabet,* signed by Georges Auric, setting to music two of the poems in this book—*Filet à papillons* and *Hirondelle.*

364. *Les Joues en feu. Poèmes anciens et poèmes inédits. 1917–1921. Précédé d'un portrait de Pablo Picasso et d'un poème de Max Jacob et d'un avant-propos de l'auteur.* Paris: Bernard Grasset, Éditeur, 1925. 8vo, original wrappers, uncut and unopened. First complete edition. One of 1,100 numbered copies on *vélin pur fil.*

365. Telegram from Jean Cocteau to Jean Hugo, dated 9:45 a.m., 12 December 1923, announcing Radiguet's serious illness (from which he was to die later that day).

366. *Il y a trente ans* by Valentine Hugo. Holograph manuscript signed, November 1953, 36 pp.

Valentine Hugo and her husband Jean Hugo, both painters, had been close friends of Radiguet. This memoir, written thirty years after Radiguet's death, recalls that friendship.

367. *Raymond Radiguet* by Irène Lagut. Pen-and-ink sketch signed. Measures 10¾″ x 8¼″ (sheet size). Annotation in lower margin, "Non mon poète n'est pas mort," and on verso, "J'ai exécuté ce portrait aux environs de 1925."

368

370

368. *Les joues en feu. Trois poèmes de Raymond Radiguet. (Juin-Juillet 1920)* by Georges Auric. Holograph music manuscript signed, 12 pp. Folio. The score was dedicated to Irène Lagut, and this manuscript, from which the score was printed, bears the following inscription in Auric's hand: "A Irène Lagut, ces 'devoirs de vacance' [sic] / de son ami fidèle / Georges Auric / 21 octobre 1920."

369. *Les joues en feu. Trois poèmes de Raymond Radiguet* by Georges Auric. Paris: Éditions de la Sirène, 1921. Folio, original wrappers, uncut. First printing. Penciled annotations on front cover in Valentine Hugo's hand.

MAURICE RAVEL

370. Festival Maurice Ravel. Letters, notes, telegrams, and other documents related to the Ciboure festival in honor of Maurice Ravel.

In the summer of 1930, the town of Ciboure in the Basses-Pyrénées, birthplace of Maurice Ravel, staged a festival in his honor. Ravel himself participated, along with his favorite singer, Madeleine Grey, and with Jacques Thibaud, Robert Casadesus, and Lucienne Lamballe of the Paris Opéra, whose dances to Ravel's music were choreographed by the former Diaghilev ballerina Madame Egorova. The event was widely covered by the local, Paris, and foreign press, and after his return to Montfort-l'Amaury, Ravel wrote to Charles Mapou, president of the Municipal Council of Ciboure and chairman of the organizing committee, that he considered the festival the most moving event of his entire career.

During his work on the festival, M. Mapou assembled a comprehensive documentation—the letters, notes, and telegrams shown here from Ravel and the other major participants, along with additional letters and documents from Gabriel Astruc, Joaquin Nin, Émile Vuillermoz, and others, contemporary photographs of Ravel and his friends, a corrected proof of the handbill and the festival poster, as well as the complete file of the newspaper coverage.

371. *Concerto pour piano et orchestre.* Paris: Durand, 1932. Folio, loose in sheets within original printed silver wrappers. First printing. Inscribed:

à Émile Vuillermoz / Maurice Ravel / 31/12/31.

372. Photograph of Ravel at his piano. Inscribed:

à Jean-Aubry / cordialement / MR / certifié à peu près conforme / Maurice · Ravel.

373. *Un Coup de dés jamais n'abolira le hasard.* Series of 3 original lithographs executed by Redon as illustrations for Mallarmé's text, but never published. Redon originally produced four lithographs, but the printer lost one of the stones; hence proofs of only three have survived:

Femme de profil vers la gauche, coiffée d'un hennin (Mellerio 186).

Tête d'enfant, de face, avec au-dessus un arc-en-ciel (M. 187).

Femme coiffée d'une toque et rejetant le buste en arrière (M. 188).

All three proofs are on China paper. The first two are signed in the stone with the artist's monogram.

Ambroise Vollard planned to publish the book, but the printers, Firmin-Didot, refused to set up Mallarmé's text with its carefully elaborated unconventional typographical pattern. It was the work of a madman, they insisted. As a result, like so many other of Vollard's projects, this one was simply set aside and he died without having published it.

373

374. *La Tentation de Saint-Antoine* by Gustave Flaubert [Paris: Les Amis de Redon, 1935]. Folio, loose in sheets within original wrappers, uncut, in board case.

Edition limited to 130 numbered copies on *papier Maillol filigrané*, made by Gaspard Maillol. Illustrated with all three series of the lithographs, totaling forty plates, which Redon made as "interpretations" of this book.

In a letter to André Mellerio (21 July 1898) Redon wrote that it was his friend Émile Hennequin who brought him a copy of *La Tentation de Saint-Antoine* saying that Redon would find there "new monsters." He was soon captivated "by the descriptive part of this work, by the relief and color of all those resurrections of a past."

375. Holograph letter signed to G. Jean-Aubry, 23 December 1914, 7 pp.

How far away art is. . . . Mine is part of a period which is surely drawing to a close; but I should like to have been of help in opening up the new age. . . . Make way for the young . . . for emotion, sensibility, imagination, dream—for the unknown. . . .

376. Photograph of Redon seated in his atelier, by Dornac. Inscribed on verso:

. . . *pas si jeune qu'on veut bien le dire* . . . / *offert tout de même à Jean Aubry, / en souvenir amical de son attention / d'aujourd'hui, 20 avril 1915. / Odilon Redon.*

PIERRE-AUGUSTE RENOIR

377. 13 holograph letters signed to his wife (2), to Cézanne's daughter-in-law, Renée (1), and to Renée's father, Georges Rivière, art critic and biographer of Renoir (10). 1908–1917.

At Renoir's suggestion, Georges Rivière published a paper called *L'Impressionniste* during the third Impressionist exhibition in 1877, to promote the group's work and to defend it against such hostile critics as Albert Woolf of *Le Figaro*. (This was the first exhibition in which they had used the term "Impressionist," which had originally been applied to them as a form of ridicule.) Most of the articles in *L'Impressionniste* were written by Rivière; a few, signed "a painter," were by Renoir. In one of his articles Rivière spoke of the group's "treating a subject for its color values and not for the subject itself," thus pointing up Impressionism's essential originality.

378. *Le Peintre-Graveur Illustré. Tome Dix-septième. Camille Pissarro, Auguste Renoir, Alfred Sisley* by Loÿs Delteil. Paris, 1923. 4to, original wrappers, uncut and unopened.

The complete catalogue of the graphic work, with each piece illustrated, and with two original etchings: *Marché aux légumes, à Pontoise* (L. D. 97) by Pissarro, and *Sur la plage à Berneval* (L. D. 5) by Renoir.

Japan-paper issue, of which 76 copies were printed, this one marked, in Delteil's hand:

Exemplaire imprimé pour Monsieur Georges Rivière, Loïjs Delteil.

Laid in is a holograph letter signed from Delteil to Rivière, 15 January 1923, concerning Delteil's work on the book.

379. *Renoir et ses amis* by Georges Rivière. Paris: H. Floury, Éditeur, 1921. 4to, original illustrated wrappers, uncut.

One of 150 large-paper copies on *papier du Japon*, with six additional illustrations not in the regular edition and with an original drypoint by Renoir, *Le Chapeau épinglé* (*La Fille de Berthe Morisot et sa cousine*), 3e planche (L. D. 8) in two states. Daragnès bookplate.

380. *Portrait de Renoir* by Pierre Bonnard. Original etching, ca. 1914. Signed in the plate. (Terrasse 63; Johnson 20.)

PIERRE REVERDY

According to Max Jacob, Pierre Reverdy made a poem the way a good painter makes a picture: thought was kept in its proper place—present but silent.

381. *Fait divers.* Holograph manuscript signed.

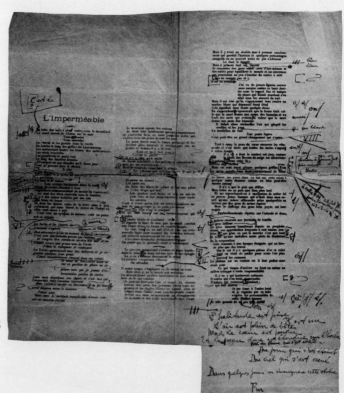

382. *Portrait.* Holograph manuscript signed.

383. *Pente.* Holograph manuscript signed.

384. *Médaillon avec cadres.* Holograph manuscript signed, 2 pp.

385. *L'Imperméable.* Corrected proof of the final installment, as it appeared in the review *SIC*.

386. 14 holograph letters signed to Pierre Albert-Birot, 1916–1918. Concerning his work and the complex politics of the Paris avant-garde: Apollinaire, Max Jacob, Paul Dermée, Roch Grey.

ARTHUR RIMBAUD

387. *Une Saison en enfer.* Bruxelles: Alliance Typographique (M.-J. Poot et Compagnie), 1873. 12mo, full black crushed levant with mosaic decoration formed by the letters of the title inlaid in contrasting colors and textures, doublures and end-leaves of red and blue suede, all edges and decorative accents in platinum, original wrappers bound in, uncut, within matching sleeve and slipcase (binding by Rose Adler).

> First edition of Rimbaud's first book, the only one published by his own initiative. Two hundred and fifty copies were printed and for many years it was thought that Rimbaud had destroyed most of them. But in 1901 the bulk of the edition was discovered in the storeroom of the printer, with whom Rimbaud had left it and who had never been paid. A large number of copies had been ruined by rust and rot and these were burned in the presence of a notary.

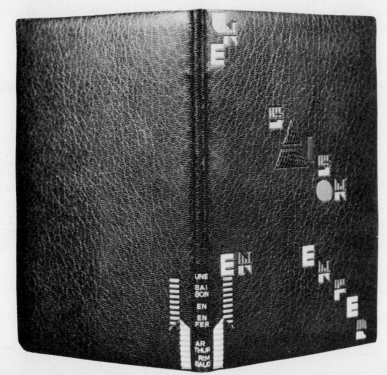

387

388. *Les Illuminations. Notice par Paul Verlaine.* Paris: Publications de La Vogue, 1886. 8vo, full crushed cyclamen levant, with inlaid and gold-stamped decoration of classical simplicity, doublures and end-leaves of vermilion suede, all edges gilt, within matching sleeve and slipcase (binding by Rose Adler).

> First edition. One of 170 numbered copies on *papier de Hollande.* By 1886 Rimbaud had long since dropped from sight and most assumed he was dead. Verlaine, with the help of letters, manuscript copies, and his recollections, had published some of Rimbaud's poems (see PAUL VERLAINE, no. 509). He had tried unsuccessfully for a number of years to retrieve the (partial) manuscript of *Les Illuminations* from his brother-in-law, the musician Charles de Sivry. In 1886 that manuscript finally reached Gustave Kahn, who published it in the review *La Vogue* (Nos. 5–9, May-June 1886) and later, in a different order, in book form. The work would appear, from internal evidence, to have been written—at least in large part—before *Une Saison en enfer.*

389. *Reliquaire. Poésies. Préface de Rodolphe Darzens.* Paris: L. Genonceaux, Éditeur, 1891. 12mo, original wrappers, uncut.

> First edition, of which 550 copies were printed in all. First-issue copy, with the 1891 date and the preface (later excised) by Darzens. The core of this first edition of Rimbaud's poems was the manuscript which Rimbaud had left in Douai with his friend Paul Demeny in October 1870. The book appeared as Rimbaud lay dying in a hospital in Marseilles. On 11 November 1891, the day after Rimbaud's death, the book was seized. The preface pleased no one—not even Darzens. Without the preface and with a new title-page, the book was reissued in 1892.

The collections of the Humanities Research Center include many unpublished documents relating to Rimbaud's life and poetry: manuscripts, letters, drawings, corrected proofs and similar material by Rimbaud's sister Isabelle; his brother-in-law Paterne Berrichon, poet and artist; his teacher Georges Izambard; Paul Verlaine; Stéphane Mallarmé; Paul Claudel, and others. The following pieces have been selected from that group.

390. Holograph letter draft from Paterne Berrichon to Francis Jammes, 2½ pp. Jammes had written protesting against what he took to be an unfair reference to Remy de Gourmont in Berrichon's *Vie de Jean-Arthur Rimbaud.* Berrichon gives Jammes details concerning the development of his interest in Rimbaud's work, his marriage to Isabelle Rimbaud, and his long friendship with Verlaine, which enabled him to destroy some of the "defamatory myths concerning Rimbaud's literary life." He places the blame for the misunderstanding on Gourmont's attack on Rimbaud in *Le Livre des masques.*

391. Holograph letter signed "Dufour-Rimbaud" from Paterne Berrichon to the director of *Le Temps,* 13 January 1913, 1½ pp. Protests against the calumny of Rimbaud in an article the paper had printed about Rimbaud's manuscripts.

392. 3 holograph letters signed "Pierre Dufour" (Berrichon's real name) to the mother of Arthur Rimbaud, April–May 1897. He writes as a hopeful and solicitous son-in-law candidate.

393. *A propos de la nouvelle édition des Oeuvres de Rimbaud* by Paterne Berrichon. Holograph manuscript signed, Roche, 8 September 1913, 7 pp. Folio.

394. *A propos de la nouvelle édition des Oeuvres de Rimbaud.* Corrected proofs of this article by Berrichon, an attack on Marcel Coulon.

395. 3 holograph letters signed from Berrichon to Alfred Vallette, director of the *Mercure de France*, 1897–1914, 5 pp. A discussion of poems and manuscripts of Rimbaud; a further attack on Marcel Coulon for his "diabolical deformations" of certain texts of Rimbaud; details of the publication of Berrichon's *Vie de Jean-Arthur Rimbaud.*

396. 5 original drawings by Berrichon:

The Village of Roche. Pencil. 4⅞″ x 8⅛″. Signed, upper left, "Roche ler août 97, PB." This drawing was done in the attic room where Rimbaud wrote *Une Saison en enfer.*

Arthur Rimbaud in London. Pencil. 10″ x 7″. Signed "Paterne B."

Head of Isabelle Rimbaud. Pencil. 8⅜″ x 5″.

Isabelle Rimbaud. Pencil. 12⅛″ x 9¾″.

Isabelle Rimbaud Reading by Her Brother Arthur's Bed. Pencil on gray-blue Vidalon paper. 12¼″ x 9½″.

396

397. Dossier relating to the first monument to Rimbaud, erected at Charleville in 1901 and destroyed by the Germans in World War I.

* Holograph letter signed by Berrichon and Ernest Delahaye, 11 March 1901, 2 pp., on stationery imprinted *Monument à Arthur Rimbaud*, soliciting contributions for the project.

* Subscription lists, 15 pp.

* Cloth-bound notebook listing, in Berrichon's hand, names of donors and amounts given (among many others—Pierre Louÿs, 30 francs; Fantin-Latour, 25; Rodin, 20; Gide, 20; Pissarro, 100, largest individual contribution), 11 pp.

* 2 scale drawings, 13¾" x 9⅝", of variant proposed forms of the pedestal.

* 3 photographs of the bust (by Berrichon) and 1 of the finished monument at the unveiling.

398. *Correspondances, Les Phares, Don Juan aux enfers*, etc. Manuscript copies, in Berrichon's hand, of some of Baudelaire's best-known poems, 18 pp. 8vo, in folder inscribed "Baudelaire."

399. Contemporary photograph of Paterne Berrichon painting.

400. Holograph manuscript by Isabelle Rimbaud, 2¼ pp., concerning an account book kept by her mother between 1853 and 1882. Folio. On verso, holograph manuscript by Berrichon, 3 pp. Extract from a draft of his work on Rimbaud.

401. 10 holograph letters signed from Isabelle Rimbaud to her nephew Léon, son of Frédéric (brother of Isabelle and Arthur), August 1907–September 1912, 40 pp. Like his uncle Arthur, Léon Rimbaud was a rebellious boy and a wanderer. He had left home and maintained only sporadic contact with his family. The family had not known where to write to tell him of the death of his paternal grandmother. As a result he did not attend the funeral. Isabelle admonishes him to mull over the advice his grandmother had given him and to do her the honor of following the path she had pointed out to him. In another letter she writes to him "in the name of your uncle, Arthur Rimbaud," begging him to carry with dignity the name of Rimbaud, "you who were of so much concern to your uncle Arthur, small though you were when he left the world. . . ." The letters refer often to M. and Mme. [Paul] Signac and to [Victor] Segalen and [Maximilien] Luce.

402. *Les Illuminations* by Isabelle Rimbaud. Holograph manuscript, heavily corrected, 15½ pp. Folio. This paper appeared in the *Mercure de France* under the title *Rimbaud mystique: "Les Illuminations" et "La Chasse spirituelle."* Then, as *Rimbaud catholique*, it was included in her book *Reliques*.

403. *Reliquiae* by Isabelle Rimbaud. Manuscript with hand-printed variant title-page, of *Reliques*, Isabelle Rimbaud's monument to her brother Arthur, 115 pp. This manuscript was used in printing the first edition of the book (Paris: Mercure de France, 1921) and consists of manuscript in the hand of Paterne Berrichon, typed sheets, and printed excerpts cut from those portions of the book which had previously appeared in the magazine *Mercure de France*. Accompanying the manuscript are holograph additions by Nicolette Hennique and Marguerite Yerta-Méléra, 8 pp. Folio.

404. *Reliques.* 3 sets of corrected proofs of the book, one in galleys, the others (successive states) in the form of unsewn sheets.

405. *Le Dernier voyage de Rimbaud* by Isabelle Rimbaud. Typescript, Charleville, 1897, 15 pp.

406. Autograph manuscript in two unidentified hands, listing the contents of all papers relating to Arthur Rimbaud in the possession, at that time, of the Rimbaud family, 8 pp. Folio. Divided into the following groups:

    1 – Dossier Arthur Rimbaud
    2 –   "   Mme. Vve. Rimbaud
    3 –   "   Vitalie Rimbaud
    4 –   "   Isabelle Rimbaud

        Dossiers africains

    5 – Dossier Soleillet et Pino
    6 –   "   Ilg
    7 –   "   Zimmerman
    8 –   "   Savouré
    9 –   "   Sottiro
   10 –   "   des religieux
10 bis –   "   Borelli
   11 –   "   Bardey
   12 –   "   César Tian
   13 –   "   Labatut
   14 –   "   Suel
14 bis –   "   Bienfeld [sic]
   15 –   "   Riès
   16 –   "   Righaz

        Dossiers Berrichon

407. 4 holograph letters signed from Pierre Albin to Paterne Berrichon, 6½ pp. Concerning Rimbaud's death, with extracts from the records of the Hôpital de la Conception in Marseilles.

408. 4 holograph letters signed from Paul Claudel, 3 from his wife, and 1 from his assistant, Philippe Berthelot, to Paterne Berrichon, 1917–1919, 21 pp. Concerning the estate of Isabelle Rimbaud and the legal and financial problems created by her having named Claudel, along with her husband, to share in it. After some shrewd reservations, Claudel accepts, "in memory of Arthur Rimbaud and his sister," but these letters give rise to a number of questions about Isabelle's intentions and Claudel's sincerity. They point up, as do other papers in this collection, the unremitting efforts of Isabelle Rimbaud to keep her brother, even after her own death, on the side of the angels. Few other corpses in the history of literature can have been fought over as intensely as Rimbaud's. Other documents in the collection show how bitterly some of the other celebrants fought; in fact, nearly all who were touched by the magic of Rimbaud's poetry and the mystique of his life wanted to make him theirs and to mold of him an image based principally on their own desires.

409. Holograph letter signed by René Ghil, 1½ pp. Together with a copy in his hand of extracts concerning Rimbaud's brief service in the Dutch East Indian Army taken from the records of the (Dutch colonial) war registry by a friend of Ghil's in Batavia, Java.

410. Holograph letter signed from Louise Herding (nurse) to Paterne Berrichon, 11 pp. Concerning the last days and death of Isabelle Rimbaud.

411. Holograph letter signed from Stéphane Mallarmé to Arthur Rimbaud's mother, 25 March 1897, 6 pp. (retained corrected draft). In reply to her inquiry about the suitability of Paterne Berrichon as a husband for her daughter Isabelle, Mallarmé compares Berrichon's rebellious young manhood to Rimbaud's.

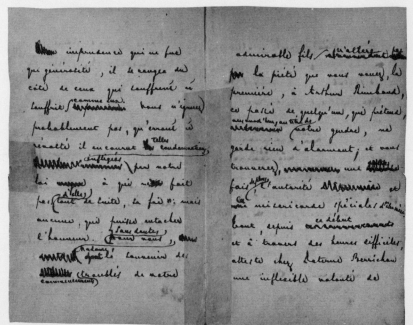

CHRONIQUE

Arthur Rimbaud

texte et dessins par Paul Verlaine

Il y a quelques mois, à l'occasion d'un monument tout simple qu'on élevait à Mürger dans le Luxembourg, j'écrivais même quelques lignes qu'on a taxées dans certains milieux, un peu bien grincheux, faut l'avouer, « de complaisance » à qui et pour qui, grands dieux ! Et pourquoi ces soupçons, ou pour mieux dire ces semblants, ces façons, ces manières, ces grimaces de soupçons ? A cause, je le présume et le m'y tiens, de l'indulgence que j'ai, dans le cas qui m'occupait, professée envers une mémoire légère et gracieuse, quoi qu'en aient dit ces incompétents censeurs, et l'indulgence ces messieurs m'en veulent plus, étant, eux, tout d'une pièce, parfaits et ne souffrant que des gens parfaits... Il est vrai que si on les scrutait, eux enfin ! Mais passons, et sautons au sujet qui doit nous occuper quelques instants.

Il se trouve donc que quelques mois après mon article sur la bohème Mürger, j'élucubre ici un article sur je ne dirai pas le bohème Rimbaud, le mot serait faux et il vaut même mieux, mieux même, lui laisser toute son « horreur » en supprimant l'épithète !

Rimbaud ! et c'est assez !

Non. Rimbaud ne fut pas un « bohème. » Il n'en eut ni les mœurs débraillées, ni la paresse, ni aucun des défauts qu'on attribue généralement à cette caste bien vague toutefois et peu déterminée jusqu'à nos jours.

Ce fut un poète très jeune et très ardent, qui commença

A peine au sortir de l'enfance

à voyager à travers sa pittoresque contrée natale d'abord, puis parmi les paysages belges si compliqués, et enfin, gravita, au milieu des horreurs de la guerre, jusqu'à Paris, laissant derrière ses pieds infatigables la forêt de Villers-Coterets et les campagnes fortifiées, par l'ennemi, de l'Ile-de-France. Lors de ce premier voyage dans la capitale il joua une première fois de malheur, fut arrêté dès en arrivant, fourré à Mazas, au Dépôt, et finalement expulsé de Paris et rejoignant comme qui dirait de brigade en brigade sa famille alarmée, tandis que sur son passage s'émouvait encore le sillage laissé par le poète dans un monde « littéraire » qui ne le comprit pas du tout, et d'ailleurs, tout à la débandade, par suite de la guerre de 1870 qui commençait à sévir ferme. Les gens furent stupéfaits de tant de jeunesse et de talent mêlés à tant de sauvagerie et de positive lycanthropie. Les femmes elles-mêmes, les dernières grisettes (dernières ?) (grisettes ?) eurent peur du frisson

de ce gamin qui semblait ne pas, mais pas le moins du monde penser à elles !

De sorte que lorsqu'il revint à Paris, un an et plus, après, il n'y fut pas populaire, croyez-moi. Sauf un petit groupe de Parnassiens indépendants (les grands Parnassiens Coppée, Mendès, Hérédia n'admirent que mal ou pas du pré le phénomène nouveau. Valade, Mérat, Charles Cros, moi donc, il ne trouva guère d'accueil dans la capitale revisitée. Mais celui qu'il reçut là fut vraiment cordial et... effectif. L'hospitalité la plus aimable, la plus large... et la plus *circulaire*, c'est-à-dire, au fond, la plus commode de toutes, l'auteur de chacun dans l'au-jour, le jour de la saison coûteuse et glaciale, je ne crois pas qu'homme eût jamais été l'objet d'une aussi

gentille confraternité, d'une aussi délicate solidarité témoignées...

Aussi ! c'était l'auteur, jeune invraisemblablement, de vers si extraordinaires, puissants, charmants, pervers ! Il arrivait avec ce bagage précieux, spécieux, captieux ! Des idylles savoureuses de nature réelle et parfois bizarrement, mais précisément vues ; des descriptions vertigineuses vraiment géniales, le *Bateau ivre*, les *Premières Communions*, chefs-d'œuvre à mon gré d'artiste, parfois bien réprouvable pour mon âme catholique, les *Effarés* que dans l'Edition Nouvelle des *Poésies Complètes* (*) une main pieuse, sans doute, mais, à mon sens lourde et bien maladroite, en tous cas, a « corrigés » dans plusieurs passages, pour des fins antiblasphématoires bien inattendues, mais que voici intégralement dans leur texte exquis et superbe !

LES EFFARÉS

Noirs dans la neige et dans la brume
 Au grand soupirail qui s'allume,
   Leurs culs en rond,

A genoux, cinq petits — misère !

(*) chez Léon Vanier, 19, quai Saint-Michel.

Regardent le boulanger faire
 Le lourd pain blond.

Ils voient le fort bras blanc qui tourne
 La pâte grise, et qui l'enfourne
   Dans un trou clair.

Ils écoutent le bon pain cuire.
 Le boulanger au gros sourire,
   Chante un vieil air.

Ils sont blottis, pas un ne bouge,
 Au souffle du soupirail rouge
   Chaud comme un sein.

Quand, pour quelque médianoche,
 Façonné comme une brioche,
   On sort le pain ;

Quand, sur les poutres enfumées,
 Chantent les croûtes parfumées
   Et les grillons ;

Que ce trou chaud souffle la vie,
 Ils ont leur âme si ravie
   Sous leurs haillons,

Ils se ressentent si bien vivre,
 Les pauvres Jésus pleins de givre !
   Qu'ils sont là, tous,

Collant leurs petits museaux roses
 Aux grillages, grognant des choses
   Entre les trous,

Tout bêtes, faisant leurs prières
 Et repliés vers ces lumières
   Du ciel rouvert,

Si fort qu'ils crèvent leur culotte
 Et que leur chemise tremblotte
   Au vent d'hiver.

Tel est le livre qui vient de paraître chez Vanier, le plus complet possible au point de vue des vers *vraiment vrais*, ajouterai-je, et fit ensuite, c'est-à-dire tout de suite d'après sa fuite libre, non sa reconduite (cette fois-ci) de Paris, sa fuite en quelque sorte triomphale, de Paris, des vers libres superbes, encore clairs, puis telles très belles proses qu'il fallait.

Puis après avoir tenté, non pas la fortune, ni même la chance, mais le Désennui, dans des voyages néanmoins occupés en des industries pittoresques (dents d'éléphants, poudre d'or) il mourut d'une opération manquée, retour de l'Hérat, à l'Hôpital de la Conception à Marseille, dans, assure l'éditeur autorisé des *Poésies Complètes*, les sentiments de la plus sincère piété.

PAUL VERLAINE.

412. Holograph letter signed from Vittorio Pica to Paterne Berrichon, Naples, 30 November 1897, 7 pp. Pica thanks Berrichon for sending him a copy of his book on Rimbaud and tells him he is planning to publish a study of Rimbaud's poetry. He sends him "three unpublished sonnets by Arthur Rimbaud that you may not be familiar with and that I received from Verlaine ten years ago. . . ." The three sonnets, here in Pica's hand, are those that were privately printed under the title *Les Stupra* in 1923, with the date of 1871. In closing, Pica quotes part of the letter addressed to him by Verlaine on 12 January 1887: "I am writing them from memory. . . . There are a few words I am not completely certain of that I have underlined. . . ." Pica has underlined a total of ten words in the three sonnets. Aside from the words underlined, this manuscript shows a number of differences from the printed version, especially in the second sonnet. The third conforms fairly closely to the version which appeared in *Hombres* (1904).

413. 4 holograph letters signed from Ernest Raynaud to Paterne Berrichon, 7 pp. Concerning the marriage of Berrichon and Isabelle Rimbaud, Berrichon's book *La Vie de Jean-Arthur Rimbaud*, and poems of Rimbaud suppressed by Mercure de France. " 'Poison perdu' est bel et bien d'Arthur Rimbaud." (The sonnet was, in fact, by Rimbaud's friend Germain Nouveau.)

414. *Arthur Rimbaud* by Paul Verlaine. Proof of this article published in *Les Beaux-Arts* for 1 December 1895, 1 p. Folio. Text illustrated with 2 drawings of Rimbaud by Verlaine. This proof contains 16 corrections in Verlaine's hand. Together with 2 holograph letters signed from Verlaine to Léon Deschamps, the paper's editor, 21 October and 29 November 1895, concerning the article and with a note from Deschamps accepting it.

> The most significant influence in Rimbaud's early development was that of Georges Izambard, the promising young poet who came at the age of 21 to teach at the Collège de Charleville, where Rimbaud was a student. He encouraged and guided Rimbaud, lent him books, and later, when Rimbaud was unable to stand his home environment any longer and ran away, received him at the home of his "aunts," the Gindre sisters, in Douai. Throughout a long and varied career (he died in his eighties having been a teacher, poet, songwriter, journalist, lecturer, inventor), Izambard was in the forefront of the often heated struggles between rival camps of Rimbaldists and made important contributions to the bibliography.

Humanities Research Center collections include the following material related to Izambard's association with Rimbaud.

415. Holograph manuscripts by Izambard. A dossier beginning in 1866, four years before his meeting with Rimbaud, and carrying through until shortly before his death. The first manuscript, a collection of 13 poems dated 1866, written in a 24-page home-sewn booklet, is evidently a fair copy of earlier

drafts, as are a number of later groups and notebooks. Many poems are present in first, or early, heavily corrected drafts. There are two short plays, a number of songs, and some pieces in prose (articles, lectures, notes, etc.). Altogether, about 260 pages of manuscript.

In Rimbaud's poem *A la musique*, subtitled *Place de la Gare, Charleville*, the line "Et je sens des baisers qui me viennent aux lèvres" was "given" to him by Izambard (see *Mercure de France*, 15 December 1910) as a replacement for an unsatisfactory line: "Et mes désirs brutaux s'accrochent à leurs lèvres." Jarred by the line Rimbaud had originally written, Izambard took the replacement from a short verse play he himself was working on at the moment, *Les Oreilles de Midas*, here present in a partial, revised version. In return for this, Rimbaud helped Izambard fashion a line to replace the one taken from *Les Oreilles de Midas*. Izambard later used this new line, "Et qui lui fait monter des baisers fous aux lèvres," in his poem *Le Baiser du faune* as shown in two variant printed versions of that poem included in the Izambard papers. The original source of *Les Oreilles de Midas* had been a line drawing entitled *Le Baiser du faune* in the Naples museum (see *La Grive*, No. 5, October 1929). The papers include a pencil sketch made by Izambard from the original drawing.

416. Autograph manuscript, signed by Henriette Gindre, of readings and other material. In the hands both of Henriette and, for a few pages, of her sister Caroline, 1848–1849, 122 pp. Folio.

It was during this period that the Gindre sisters, friends of the Izambard family, had taken the infant Georges into their home in Douai after his mother died. When Rimbaud ran away from home and twice sought out Izambard in Douai, the Gindre sisters sheltered him for several weeks on each occasion until Mme. Rimbaud forced Izambard to return her son to Charleville.

The Gindre sisters are "Les Chercheuses de poux" in Rimbaud's poem of that name.

417. Letter-book of Georges Izambard with 500 pages of tissue carbon copies of letters written by him beginning in 1900. These are personal, business, and professional in content. Many are long, illustrated letters recording experiments in connection with some of Izambard's inventions in the fields of printing, photography, and radiology. A few are of Rimbaud interest: e.g., the letter of 3 March 1900, relating to an encounter with his (and Rimbaud's) friend Paul Demeny, to whom Rimbaud addressed the famous *Lettre du voyant* (15 May 1871); a 5-page letter entitled *Note sur l'Affaire Gindre, pour être remise à Me. Amy, notaire*; and an 8-page letter dated Passy-Paris, 22 November 1905 in another hand, noted as signed by Henriette Gindre, and concerning the ownership of the Gindre house in Douai where Izambard was reared and Rimbaud had stayed.

418. Letter from Rimbaud to Izambard, dated "2 novembre, 1870." Manuscript copy by Izambard, 2 pp.

419. *Collection des inédits. Georges Izambard. Édition critique des Oeuvres de Rimbaud. I. Rimbaud à Charleville et à Douai.* Holograph manuscript and corrected typescript of the work published in 1928 by Kra in Paris as: *Arthur Rimbaud. A Douai et à Charleville. Lettres et écrits inédits. Commentés par Georges Izambard.* This edition was limited to 600 copies. Twenty lines are missing at the beginning of the second section, but the manuscript contains additional material omitted from the published version.

420. 4 typewritten letters signed, 1 holograph letter signed, and a telegram from Philippe Soupault to Izambard, 1926–1927, 8 pp. 4to. Concerning the above-mentioned book. Soupault was, at the time, an editor for the publisher Kra.

421. *Rimbaud* by Georges Gorvel. Original engraving. Proof on Japan paper.

422. *Portrait de Rimbaud* by René Henry-Munsch. Original woodcut.

AUGUSTE RODIN

423. 6 holograph letters signed and 1 holograph postcard signed to Léopold Hugo (nephew of Victor Hugo), 1890–1892. Concerning Rodin's *Balzac* and the project for a monument to Victor Hugo.

424. Autograph letter signed to Armand Dayot [1915], 9 pp. Folio. An eloquent plea for the preservation of French cathedrals against the dual barbarisms of neglect and improper restoration.

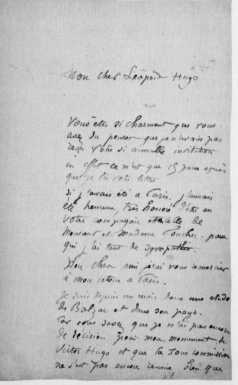

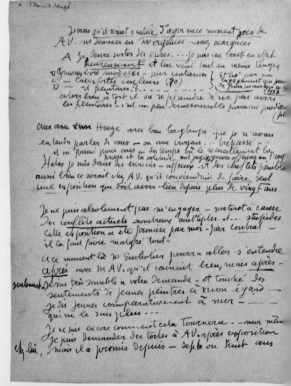

423   429

425. Original drypoint (1916) engraved for fund-raising campaign of the American Hospital in Paris.

426. Holograph manuscript by Émile-Antoine Bourdelle, 19 pp.

In 1903, when Rodin was named Commander of the Légion d'Honneur, his friends and pupils honored him with a banquet, at which Isadora Duncan danced. As a former assistant, pupil, and collaborator, and now as Rodin's devoted friend and nearest-equal as a sculptor, Bourdelle gave the keynote speech and toast which make up this manuscript.

427. *Rodin* by Giorgio Kienerk. Sepia drawing. Measures 9⅝" x 6⅜".

GEORGES ROUAULT

428. 9 holograph letters signed by Rouault to his engraver M. Chaperont, and 9 by Rouault's daughter Isabelle, writing in her father's behalf, to M. Chaperont, 1934. Letters include detailed instructions ("Do nothing without me") for the printing of his color etchings *Parade* and *L'Automne*. One is written on a letter addressed to Rouault by his dealer, Ambroise Vollard, in which Vollard urges Rouault to finish the paintings and wood engravings which will be used to illustrate the *Passion* he plans to publish.

429. Holograph letter signed to the painter Edmond Heuzé, 2 pp. Folio. Concerning his relations with Vollard. The contract between them made Rouault virtually an indentured servant, at least in Rouault's view. The letter ends with a long passage of lamentations, a poem-prayer entitled *Miserere* in which he asks to be spared the anguish brought on by facile criticism, futile denials, certain politicians of art, and the merchants of the temple. This letter might be considered a Rouault anthology.

430. Unpublished wood engraving, unique trial proof. Measures 11¾" x 7¾". An illustration for the title-page of Vollard's *Les Réincarnations du Père Ubu* (Paris: Ambroise Vollard, 1932 [1933]), on which Rouault began working before 1916. This composition was discarded in favor of a smaller one, less handsome by far, but more appropriate to the layout.

431. 4 original aquatints from the series Rouault made for *Les Réincarnations du Père Ubu*. Fine early proofs (1918), with the *vient de paraître* stamp used in publicizing the book.

432. 5 trial proofs of woodblocks used in the printing of Rouault's *Cirque de l'Étoile Filante* (Paris: Ambroise Vollard, 1938 [1939]): 2 variants of the *ecuyère* motif, a Pierrot, a *trois grotesques*, and a seal built around Rouault's initials, used in red on the book's cover. A unique set, printed on thin Japan paper.

430

COURRIER   SUD

d'après le roman

d'ANTOINE DE SAINT-EXUPERY

Scénario & Découpage de

A. de St-EXUPERY

H. G. LUSTIG

R. BRESSON

Dialogues de A. de St-EXUPERY

Mise en scène de Pierre BILLON

PRODUCTION

PAN-CINE

435

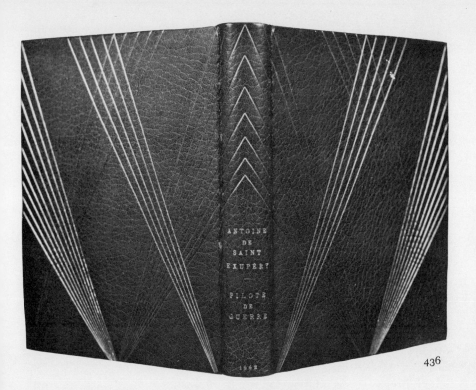

436

439

The first four woodblocks were drawn by Rouault and cut by his collaborator, Georges Aubert; the fifth was drawn and cut by Rouault, the only block known to have been cut by him. The first three are signed in the block with Rouault's monogram and dated 1935; the fourth is signed in the block with his initials and dated 1932. The first three measure (image only) approximately 2½″ x 1½″; the fourth, 1¼″ x 2⅞″.

433. Original woodblock (the fifth woodblock mentioned in item 432, above) cut by Rouault. Measures 2 11-16″x 2 7-8″.

ANTOINE DE SAINT-EXUPÉRY

434. *Courrier Sud.* Paris: N. R. F. [Nouvelle Revue Française], 1929. 8vo, original wrappers, uncut. First edition of Saint-Exupéry's first book. Review copy, with a presentation inscription from the author to Émile Vuillermoz.

435. *Courrier Sud.* Mimeographed typescript, scenario of the film version, directed by Pierre Billon, 155 pp. Folio. One of a very small number of copies mimeographed for use during the filming. This one was Saint-Exupéry's working copy and has corrections, additions, and a number of deletions in his hand. The scenario was written by Saint-Exupéry, H. G. Lustig, and Robert Bresson. Presentation inscription from Saint-Exupéry on the title-page:

> *Pour Cami Delange / et son René / avec toute ma vieille amitié / A. de Saint-Exupéry.*

436. *Pilote de guerre.* New York: Éditions de la Maison Française (1942). 4to, full blue crushed levant, with decorative pattern on both covers and backstrip formed of intersecting gilt lines symbolizing antiaircraft batteries sweeping the skies, doublures and end-leaves of matching blue suede, within double gilt-framed border, all edges gilt, original wrappers bound in, uncut. Within matching half-morocco sleeve and slipcase (binding by Lobstein).

First edition. One of 25 lettered, large-paper copies, not for sale, on Strathmore paper. This copy was printed for Saint-Exupéry's wife: "Exemplaire spéciale-ment imprimé pour la Comtesse Antoine de Saint-Exupéry." Beneath that the author has written:

> *Avec toute ma tendresse pour / la petite Consuelo. / Antoine.*

437. *Le Petit Prince. Avec dessins par l'auteur.* New York: Reynal and Hitch-cock (1943). Small 4to, original pictorial wrappers. First edition.

438. *Le Petit Prince.* Typescript (carbon) of an unrevised version, with minor changes and several pencil drawings in Saint-Exupéry's hand and with other annotations.

439. *Le Petit Prince.* Two original watercolors by Saint-Exupéry: one of the Little Prince, the other of the Baobab, both with annotations in Saint-Exupéry's hand. Each measures approximately 11″ x 8½″. One is a trial version of the full-page illustration opposite page 14 of *Le Petit Prince* (also used on the book's cover); the other is a trial version of the illustration opposite page 22. Both vary substantially from the published versions.

SAINT-JOHN PERSE

In his first book, *Éloges*, Saint-John Perse, a poet of epic scope, looks back to his childhood in the Antilles. In the process he sketches in suggestions of the themes that will inform all his other books. The publication of *Éloges* marked him as a major poet, and his art (as Paul Morand later put it) seemed a "new romanticism, as demanding, as concise, as the purest classic."

Eighteen of the poems had first appeared in the N.R.F. review, badly scarred by typographical errors. As a gesture of atonement, André Gide, the principal founding father of the N.R.F., arranged for immediate publication of the corrected text in book form. When the book reached Gide, he kept reading it, over and over, each time with mounting joy. It distilled for him, he wrote to Jacques Rivière, a kind of "fermented syrup" that went to his head and his heart.

440. *Éloges* by Saintléger Léger. Paris: Nouvelle Revue Française / Marcel Rivière & Cie. [1911]. 12mo, full morocco, raised bands, top edges gilt, original wrappers bound in (binding by Malcorps).

First edition, issued under a name which is a slight variant of Saint-John Perse's real name (Alexis Saint-Léger Léger). Includes *Éloge III*, omitted from later editions.

441. *Éloges* by St.-J. Perse. Paris: Librairie Gallimard / Nouvelle Revue Française [1925]. 4to, three-quarter morocco, raised bands, top edges gilt, original wrappers bound in (binding by Malcorps).

Second edition, containing in addition to the poems in the first edition (with the exception of *Éloge III*): *Amitié du prince, Histoire du régent, Images à Crusoé*, and *Écrit sur la porte*.

442. *Éloges* by St.-J. Perse. [Paris] Gallimard [1948]. 4to, original wrappers, uncut and unopened.

Third (and first complete) edition. One of 25 numbered large-paper copies on *vélin pur fil*. The text is here arranged in a new order; the poem *Berceuse* has been added; other poems have been retitled, and a bibliographical note added.

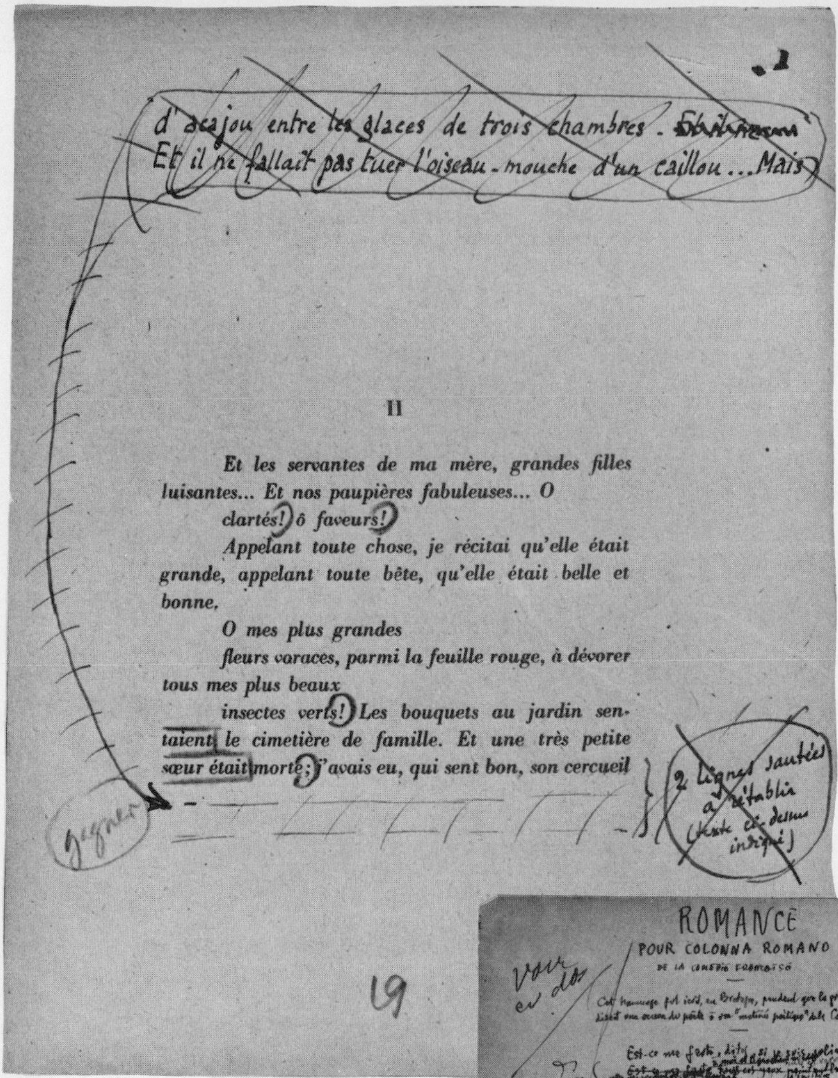

d'acajou entre les glaces de trois chambres. ~~Et il faut~~
Et il ne fallait pas tuer l'oiseau-mouche d'un caillou... Mais

II

Et les servantes de ma mère, grandes filles
luisantes... Et nos paupières fabuleuses... O
clartés! ô faveurs!

Appelant toute chose, je récitai qu'elle était
grande, appelant toute bête, qu'elle était belle et
bonne,

O mes plus grandes
fleurs voraces, parmi la feuille rouge, à dévorer
tous mes plus beaux
insectes verts! Les bouquets au jardin sen-
taient le cimetière de famille. Et une très petite
sœur était morte; j'avais eu, qui sent bon, son cercueil

gagner

2 lignes sautées
à rétablir
(texte ci-dessus
indiqué)

449

49

voir
au dos

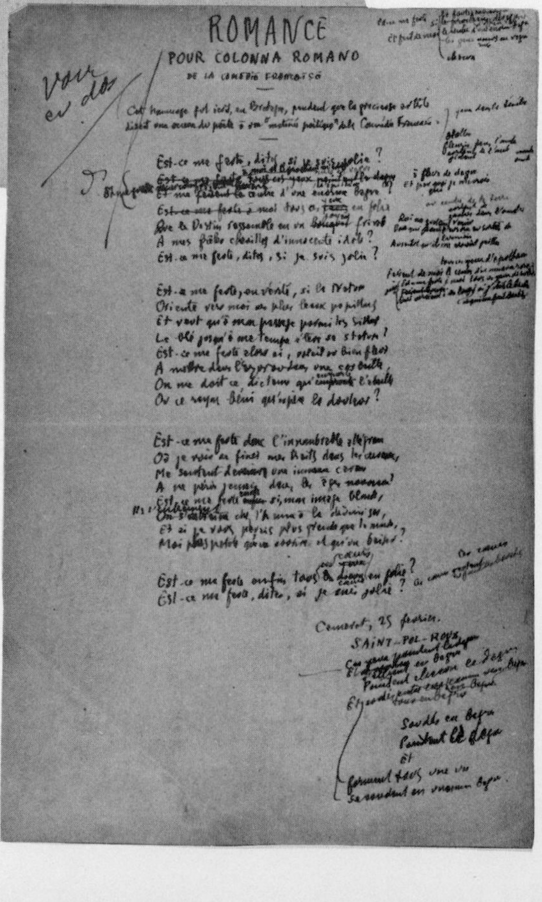

ROMANCE
POUR COLONNA ROMANO
DE LA COMÉDIE FRANÇAISE

Est-ce ma faute, dites, si je suis jolie?

450

443. *Éloges*. Corrected page proofs of the third edition, embodying the holograph manuscript of the *Note bibliographique sur les publications d'Éloges*, 3 pp., 4to; together with holograph letter signed to J. Festy (head of the publisher's production department), Washington, 18 February 1948, 2 pp.; and holograph manuscript detailing the changes involved in the edition, 3 pp.

444. *Note bibliographique* [and] *Additions à la bibliographie*. 2 holograph manuscripts, 7 pp. 4to. Together with corrected tear sheets of the printed bibliography, with holograph additions.

445. Saint-John Perse's speech accepting the Nobel Prize, 10 December 1960. Typescript (carbon), with a few holograph corrections. Inscribed: "Pour mon cher [Alain] Bosquet, / très affectueusement / A. L."

446. Essay on Saint-John Perse. Typescript in French, 8 pp., with emendations in ink by Saint-John Perse. 4to. This essay appears in somewhat different form in *Saint-John Perse: Présentation par Alain Bosquet* (Paris: Seghers, 1953), in the section headed *La personne de l'auteur n'appartient pas à son public*.

447. *Introduction* by Archibald MacLeish. Manuscript copy in the hand of Saint-John Perse, of an essay about him, signed and dated "Washington, October, 1943," 5 pp. 4to. With some differences from the text which appeared under that title in *Éloges and Other Poems*, the French text with English translations by Louise Varèse (New York: W. W. Norton, 1944).

SAINT-POL-ROUX

Il convient de saluer [Saint-Pol-Roux] parmi [les vivants]
comme le seul authentique précurseur du mouvement dit moderne.

André Breton
Les Nouvelles Littéraires, 9 mai 1925

448. *Loup blanc*. Holograph manuscript signed, Forêt des Ardennes, December 1895. On verso, a letter concerning the poem.

449. *Le Tombeau de Stéphane Mallarmé*. Holograph manuscript signed, 1898. During a banquet held on 23 March 1891, Mallarmé referred to Saint-Pol-Roux as "my son."

450. *Romance pour Colonna Romano, de la Comédie-Française*. Holograph manuscript signed, with many corrections, 3 pp. Folio.

On page 3 is the beginning of *La Spendeur* [sic] *humaine: Pièce en cinq actes*; on a fourth page are penciled notes, some of which concern *L'Ancienne à la coiffe innombrable*.

451. *Taï de Camaret*. Holograph manuscript, heavily corrected, 2 pp. Folio. Accompanying the manuscript is a copy of a folder entitled *Appel des canotiers du Taï aux hôtes de Camaret*, containing a text by Saint-Pol-Roux.

452. *Litanies de la mer. Invocations.* N. p., n. d. Folio, cyclostyled album. The rare first printing, consisting of a few copies turned out on a duplicating machine in reproduction of the original manuscript. Many of the lines were retraced in ink or added by hand afterward.

453. *Les Poèmes* by Gustave Kahn. Holograph manuscript, 5 pp. Oblong 8vo. A study of Saint-Pol-Roux's book *La Dame à la faulx*.

454. 2 photographs of Saint-Pol-Roux, 1 with his daughter, Divine; his carte-de-visite; and his death notice.

C.-A. SAINTE-BEUVE

455. 117 holograph letters signed to his cousin Aglaé Demont, and 3 to another Demont cousin. In addition, there are 18 related letters (mostly from Sainte-Beuve's secretary, Jules Troubat) and 2 clippings. Together, 140 pieces, 1823–1880.

Sainte-Beuve was a curious, ambivalent figure: a model of industry in sorting out the literary monuments of the past, but not always as generous or even as perceptive as he might have been in dealing with his contemporaries—forever picking away at the "vulgarity" of Balzac, indifferent to the major virtues of Stendhal and Flaubert, blind to the qualities of Gérard de Nerval, and somewhat condescending toward Baudelaire. In the present correspondence, entirely unpublished, he appears rather gentle, at moments almost attractive.

456. *Joseph Lebon*. Holograph manuscript, 31 pp. Folio. Synopsis for an unpublished play based on the French Revolution, with additional notes on verso of some of the sheets.

> The systematic manner in which Sartre has drawn up this synopsis would indicate that it was a project to which he had attached considerable importance. The first 17 pages give a detailed account, act by act, of the story. This is followed by four pages of notes on the period, four more summarizing the chief events in Lebon's life, and a final six defining the character of Lebon and that of his mistress.
>
> Lebon had known Robespierre before the Revolution and followed him into action in 1789. In 1793 Lebon was accused by a Revolutionary tribunal of being too lenient in his judgments but was not punished. Over the next two years his policies changed so radically as to bring on a second trial, which resulted in his being condemned for brutality and guillotined.
>
> Other Revolutionary figures who appear in Sartre's scenario include Schneider, Jacques Roux, and Hébert.

457. *Liberté—Égalité*. Holograph manuscript, 53 pp. Folio. Draft of a philosophical and historical study of the French Revolution.

458. Holograph manuscript, 31 pp. Folio. Draft of Sartre's analysis of the Peace Conference held in Vienna in 1952, in which he played a leading role.

459. Dossier of manuscript material relating to the Vienna Peace Conference of 1952. 16 pieces by Sartre and others, documenting Sartre's efforts to rally support for the Congress among non-Communist writers and intellectuals, so that the cause of peace should not seem to have become the exclusive property of the Communist propaganda machine. The dossier includes his holograph draft of the circular letter which he sent out with that intention to Michel Leiris, Robert Merle, Maurice Druon and others; their replies; a related holograph letter signed from Sartre to Aragon; and similar material.

460. *Socialisme ou barbarie*. Holograph manuscript, 34 pp. Folio.

461. *Saint Genet, comédien et martyr*. Holograph manuscript draft, 20 pp., for the early part of this monumental work by Sartre on Jean Genet. Folio.

462. Contracts signed by Sartre for editions of *La Nausée, Le Mur, Essais critiques, Entretiens sur la politique*, and his study of Baudelaire.

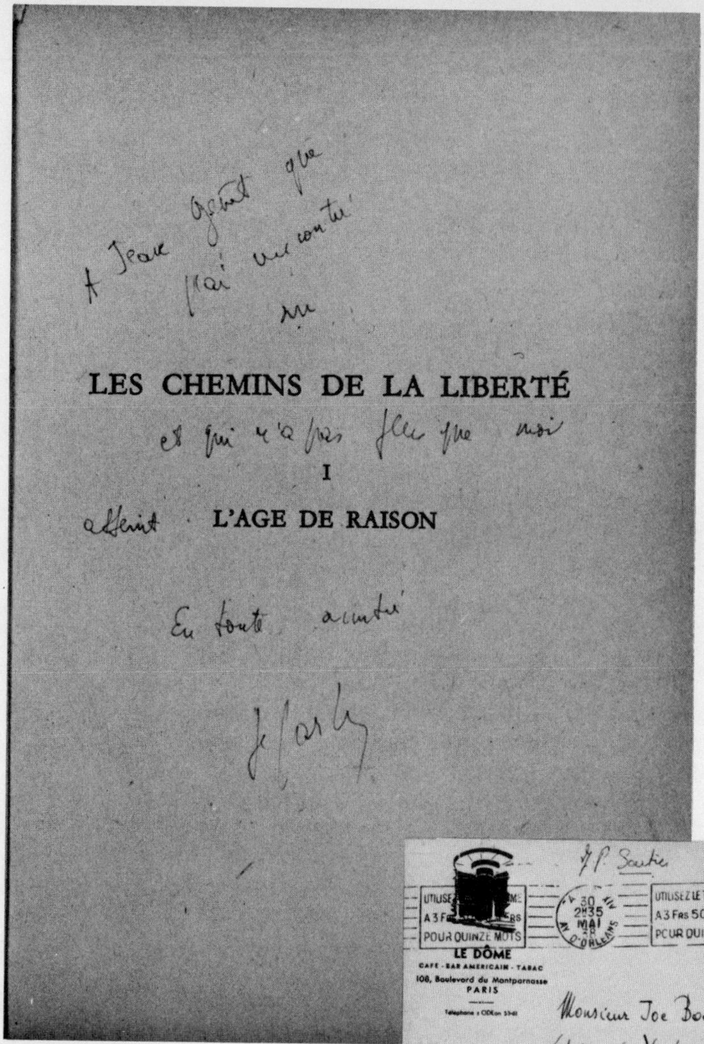

A Jean Genet que
j'ai rencontré
en

LES CHEMINS DE LA LIBERTÉ

et qui n'a pas plus que moi

I

atteint L'AGE DE RAISON

En toute amitié

JPSartre

463

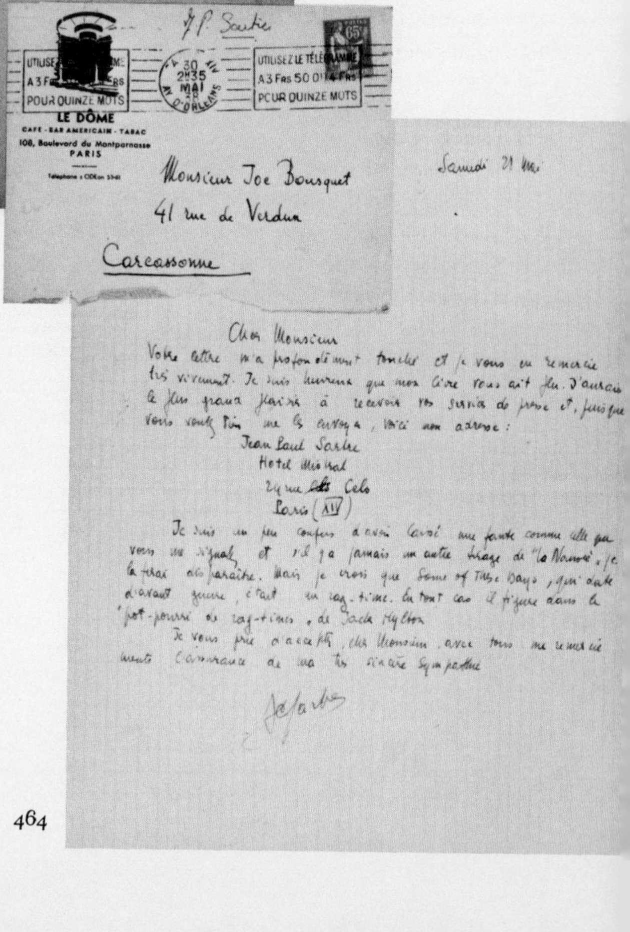

J.P. Sartre

UTILISEZ LE TÉLÉGRAMME A 3 FRS 50 OU 4 FRS POUR QUINZE MOTS

LE DÔME
CAFE - BAR AMERICAIN - TABAC
108, Boulevard du Montparnasse
PARIS
Téléphone : ODÉon 53-41

Monsieur Joë Bousquet
41 rue de Verdun
Carcassonne

Samedi 21 mai

Cher Monsieur
Votre lettre m'a profondément touché et je vous en remercie très vivement. Je suis heureux que mon livre vous ait plu. J'aurais le plus grand plaisir à recevoir vos services de presse et, puisque vous voulez bien me les envoyer, voici mon adresse :

Jean Paul Sartre
Hotel Mistral
24 rue ~~des~~ Celo
Paris (XIV)

Je suis un peu confus d'avoir laissé une faute comme celle que vous me signalez et s'il y a jamais un autre tirage de "La Nausée", je la ferai disparaître. Mais je crois que Some of These Days, qui date d'avant guerre, était un rag-time. En tout cas il figure dans le "pot-pourri de rag-times" de Jack Hylton

Je vous prie d'accepter, cher Monsieur, avec tous mes remerciements l'assurance de ma très sincère sympathie

JPSartre

464

463. *Les Chemins de la liberté. I. L'Age de raison. II. Le Sursis. III. La Mort dans l'âme* [Paris] Gallimard (1945–1949). Together 3 volumes (all published). 8vo, original wrappers, uncut and unopened.

First editions. Review copies, with the original prospectuses laid in. Volume I has the following presentation inscription on the half-title:

> A Jean Genet que / j'ai rencontré sur LES CHEMINS DE LA LIBERTÉ *et qui n'a pas plus que moi / atteint* L'AGE DE RAISON. / *En toute amitié /* J. P. Sartre.

Volume II is inscribed:

> A mon cher Jean Genet / en toute amitié / et fidèlement. / J.-P. Sartre.

Volume III has the following autograph letter laid in, from Genet to the former director of the Librairie Gallimard:

Mon cher Saucier

Je suis désolé, je n'ai pas le 3e volume des chemins de la liberté. Quant aux deux premiers, je suis encore plus désolé, car on a dû me les barbotter et vous les vendre. Jamais je n'aurais laissé circuler des livres dédicacés par Sartre. Heureusement qu'ils sont entre vos mains. Je suis plus tranquille. Si Sartre me met un mot sur le tome 3, je vous l'enverrai.

J'espère que vous et Gaston [Gallimard] allez bien. A tous deux je vous serre la main.

Jean Genet.

As noted above, all three volumes are entirely unopened.

In this trilogy, which Sartre has described as a novel about liberty and heroism, his announced intention in matters of technique was to carry on from the point at which Dos Passos, Virginia Woolf and "other novelists of simultaneity" had left off.

464. Holograph letter signed to Joë Bousquet, 28 May [1938], with printed envelope from the Café du Dôme. Thanks Bousquet for his letter about *La Nausée*. He is sorry about the error and will correct it if there is ever another printing.

465. Holograph letter signed to Jean Cocteau ("Très cher Jean Cocteau . . ."), 28 August [n. y.]. Concerning a meeting between them, which will include Simone de Beauvoir.

466. *Sartre* by André Maurois. Holograph manuscript signed, 18 pp. 4to. A concise, balanced study of Sartre's life, philosophy, novels, plays, and themes.

467. *"Relâche." Cinéma ("Entr'acte")*. Holograph music manuscript, dated by Satie at the end "Novembre 1924," 56 pp. Folio. The original, complete score for orchestra, used at the première by the conductor Roger Desormière.

The final production of Rolf de Maré's Ballets Suédois was *Relâche*, staged at Jacques Hébertot's Théâtre des Champs-Élysées on 29 November 1924, scenario and décors by Picabia, music by Erik Satie, and choreography by Jean Börlin. Picabia commissioned René Clair to create a film to be shown between the two acts of the ballet. Satie's score for the film was, in René Clair's words, "the first musical composition written for the cinema 'image by image' at a time when films were still silent." As well as being the most original part of his score for *Relâche*, *Entr'acte* is the classic example of Satie's "musique d'ameublement."

In the printed program, Picabia had written that he preferred to hear an audience protest rather than applaud. As soon as *Entr'acte* was screened, he got his wish. In spite of the hubbub, Roger Desormière continued to conduct the orchestra, and by the end of the film the shouting and whistling were offset by enthusiastic applause.

In a manifesto launched at the time of the première, Picabia wrote:

> *Entr'acte* doesn't believe in much, in the pleasure of life, perhaps; it believes in the pleasure of inventing, it respects nothing except the desire to burst out laughing, for laughing, thinking, working have the same value and are indispensable to one another.

468. 60 holograph letters and postcards, signed, to Valentine Hugo (or, before her marriage to Jean Hugo, Valentine Gross), 26 February 1914 to 7 May 1923. Fifty-eight of these letters, together with copies of certain missing letters in the hand of Valentine Hugo, many explanatory comments by her, and other related documents, have been tipped to mounts and bound in one volume. 8vo, full crimson crushed levant with inlaid design reproducing Satie's monogram in yellow on front cover, doublures and end-leaves of suede in a tone matching the monogram, within morocco-backed sleeve and slipcase (binding executed by Mercher from a design by Georges Hugnet).

The following note, in French, signed by Georges Hugnet, is inscribed on one of the blank preliminaries: "The commentaries on blue paper were written for me by Valentine Hugo (May 1955) in view of a definitive bound collection of these letters of Erik Satie."

Satie's thought and epistolary style are unique and his calligraphy is an appropriate expression of both. These letters illuminate his relations with Diaghilev, Misia Sert, Picasso, Cocteau, Fargue, Auric—especially during the years of *Parade*.

469. 2 holograph letters signed to G. Jean-Aubry, 1916–1919. In the first letter, he writes of his work on *Parade* and complains that Diaghilev, "likeable but dreadful," is driving him hard. In the second, he is agreeable to the idea of

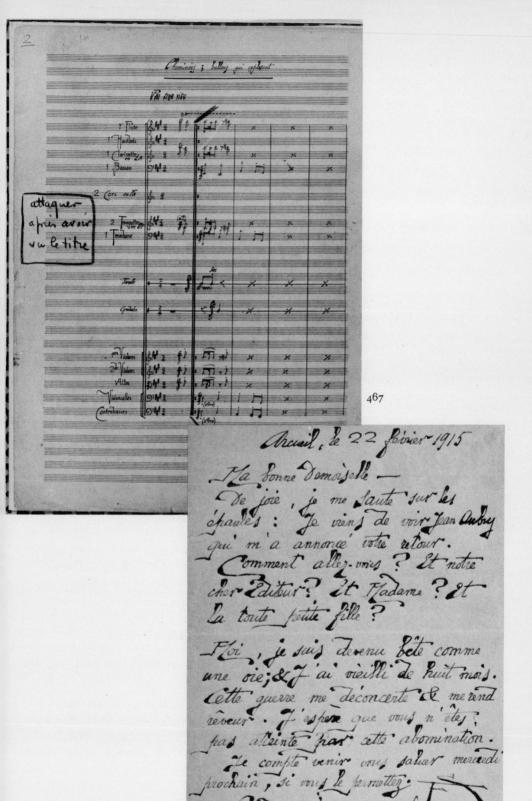

467

writing an article about Ravel, but doubts that it will please Jean-Aubry. "I like Ravel very much, but his art leaves me cold, alas!"

470. *Chapitres tournés en tous sens. Pour piano.* Paris: E. Demets, 1913. 4to, loose in sheets within original wrappers. First printing. Inscribed:

> *Au bon E. Vuillermoz / avec ses remerciements (les miens, bien / entendu). / Erik Satie.*

471. *Le Tombeau de Satie* by Henri Cliquet-Pleyel. Holograph music manuscript signed, dated "16 novembre 1926," 2 pp. and title-page. Folio. Inscribed:

> *à la mémoire d'Erik Satie.*

Cliquet-Pleyel was one of the Satie disciples of the so-called École d'Arcueil.

472. 3 pen-and-ink drawings by Jean Cocteau relating to *Parade*: 2 sketches of Erik Satie, one captioned *Le Chinois*. The third drawing, headed *Parade*, appears to be made up of design elements relating to the production, some in the form of Cocteau's initials, another based on Satie's.

473. *Le Socrate que j'ai connu* by Valentine Hugo. Holograph manuscript, 13 pp. 4to. Reminiscences of Satie by the friend he called "chère grande fille."

474. Documents concerning Erik Satie.

PAUL SIGNAC

475. Holograph letter signed to the novelist Octave Mirbeau, 23 January [n.y.], 5 pp. Folio.

An eloquent letter, which becomes a kind of profession of faith and a manifesto of the Neo-Impressionist movement. Signac discusses his influences, his aspirations, and his achievements, the Divisionist technique, and the importance of Seurat, Cézanne, and Pissarro.

GERTRUDE STEIN

476. 114 holograph letters signed, nearly all in French, to the poet Georges Hugnet, March 1928 to December 1930, 263 sides.

Hugnet translated parts of Gertrude Stein's *The Making of Americans* into French and published his edition, with a preface by himself, in 1929. In 1930 he published Stein's *Dix portraits*, which he had translated in collaboration with Virgil Thomson.

Hugnet's work had considerable influence on Gertrude Stein's poetry, as she herself acknowledged. The growth of their friendship can be measured in the progression of her salutations in these letters: "Dear Hugnet," "My dear George," "My very dear George," "My very dear little George," "My very dearest George," "My poor dear darling George." From this high point it crumbled into extinction under the impact of a clash of wills. On her own initiative and with the help of a "robust" French-English dictionary, Gertrude Stein had made translations of a sequence of poems by Hugnet which he called *Enfances*. The translations, which were to be published in the same volume as Hugnet's originals, became "adaptations" and, finally, "reflections." When the printed announcement appeared, it carried Hugnet's name and the title of the book in large type and the French equivalent of "followed by Gertrude Stein's translation" in smaller type. Gertrude Stein insisted on equal billing. Hugnet refused, since he did not view the book as a collaboration. Attempts to arbitrate their differences, with Virgil Thomson acting as mediator, failed and Gertrude Stein had her translations/reflections published by Plain Edition (i.e., Alice Toklas) under the title *Before the Flowers of Friendship Faded Friendship Faded*.

Hugnet always felt that Gertrude Stein was in love with him and that the break between them had been engineered by Alice Toklas, jealous of Gertrude's deepening interest in him.

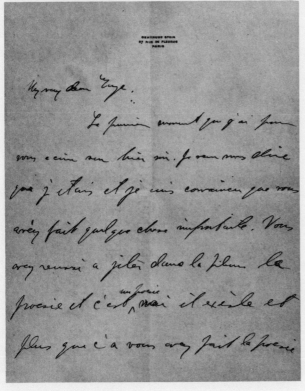

476

477. *The Making of Americans. Being a History of a Family's Progress. Written by Gertrude Stein 1906–1908* [Paris: Contact Editions, 1925]. Small 4to, original wrappers, uncut.

First edition. Five hundred copies were printed by Maurice Darantière. Some of them were imported by Albert & Charles Boni for American publication (with a different title-page and binding) in 1926.

Gertrude and Alice's copy, inscribed by Gertrude:

To us from us.

This is the copy from which Gertrude and Alice prepared the abridged edition published in 1934 by Harcourt, Brace. It had not been possible to arrange for republication of the complete work—nearly 1,000 4to pages—so they went through the entire book, marking for deletion whatever seemed expendable, then totting up the number of lines at the bottom of each page. For a writer who had always refused to allow anyone to change so much as a comma, it must have taken a massive effort of will on Gertrude Stein's part to cut herself to the bone in this fashion. There are indications of second thoughts, and toward the end the strain begins to tell: passages that had been marked for excision are questioned (the question marks are clearly Gertrude's), then restored. With this copy we see what Gertrude was willing to compromise on, what she had doubts about, and what she felt was sacrosanct in her magnum opus.

The book is housed in a loose green-cloth folder on which Gertrude Stein scrawled in pencil, "The Making."

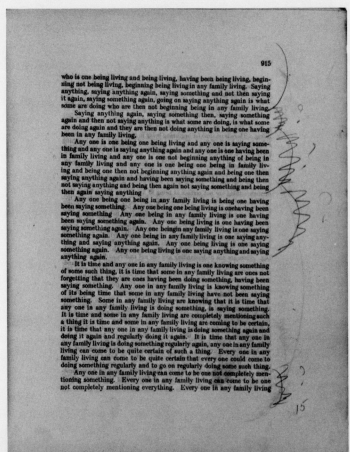

478. *The Making of Americans.* Another copy, unopened, this one from the library of Maurice Darantière, who printed the book. With his bookplate and a descriptive card in his hand.

479. *Morceaux choisis de la Fabrication des Américains. Histoire du progrès d'une famille. Traduction et préface de Georges Hugnet.* Paris: Éditions de la Montagne (1929). 8vo, original wrappers, uncut.

> First edition. One of 5 numbered copies on Japan paper—copy no. 2, signed by Gertrude Stein and Christian Bérard, whose portrait of Gertrude Stein is included in the large-paper copies.
> Gertrude and Alice's copy, with 2 four-leaf clovers pressed in. (Copy no. 1 went to Georges Hugnet.)

480. *Morceaux choisis de la Fabrication des Américains* .... Holograph manuscript of Hugnet's translation, preceded by *Préface, suivie de la Vie de Gertrude Stein et d'un Essai bibliographique*, 63 pp. Folio.

481. *Before the Flowers of Friendship Faded Friendship Faded. Written on a Poem by Georges Hugnet.* Paris: Plain Edition [1931]. Folio, original wrappers, uncut. First edition. Limited to 120 copies on Antique Montval paper. Signed by Gertrude Stein.

482. *Gertrude Stein* by Pierre Tal Coat. Pencil. Measures 16″ x 12″.

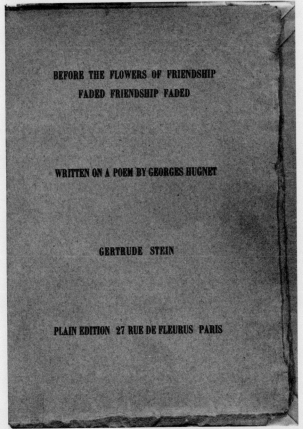

481

485

483. Papers from the family archives, consisting of 382 holograph letters signed, written by the artist, his mother, his grandmother, and other members of the immediate family and household, totaling 1,520 sides, approximately 210,000 words. Together with a notebook and an album of original drawings and sketches by Toulouse-Lautrec.

This collection of letters, entirely unpublished except for fragments of about a half-dozen of them, is the richest of sources for an understanding of Toulouse-Lautrec's formative years. The insights they provide into the family life, the character of the father and mother, their relationship with each other and with their son, enable us—in fact, compel us—to make a complete reappraisal of the effect of Lautrec's upbringing—in particular, his relationship with his mother—on his later behavior.

The family was unusually close-knit and spent much of its time visiting other units and generations in one or another of their several châteaux and country houses. When they were separated, they wrote, and these letters relate in profuse detail the interim lives they led at spas and resorts, in Paris, and with other relatives. Every one of the letters is concerned, to a greater or lesser extent, with Henri. They begin a few weeks after his birth (in 1864) and carry through until after his death (in 1901).

The most significant group—those written by Henri's mother, Adèle—passes along to her correspondents (her mother, her mother-in-law, and her sister-in-law) detailed reports of every phase of Henri's life: his health as a baby and as a young child, his early inclinations toward drawing, his interest in animals, his lessons, his accidents and medical therapy, his studies at home and with his art teachers—Princeteau, Bonnat, and Cormon. Eventually, when he is 19, he stops living with and traveling with his mother and sets out on his own. There are frequent reports of his life in Montmartre and of his visits home.

Every study or book concerned with Lautrec has taken its cue, with respect to vital matters of family relationships, from the family's own presentation of itself. Maurice Joyant, Lautrec's lifelong friend and his testamentary executor, was understandably discreet in his references to family background. And every writer since then has merely reproduced intact from his predecessors all the conventional clichés about "the gay, comfortable confusion" of Lautrec's family life and speaks of Adèle in such terms as "this sainted woman."

These evaluations have been underscored in several more recent publications by a niece of Lautrec's, who goes one step beyond that and rubs out whatever reservations one might have about Henri's father Alphonse by simply summing him up as "the incomparable sportsman." These labels are in some degree true, of course, but the real truth lies much deeper than such conventional embalming techniques would suggest, and it is in these letters that we come closest to the facts.

In a family where inbreeding was commonplace, Adèle and Alphonse were first cousins. Adèle was a romantic, sexually frigid girl, saccharine, namby-pamby, and of an exaggeratedly mawkish religiosity that would have driven any full-blooded husband or even stunted son up the wall. Her *bondieuserie* formed and clothed her every thought and provided her every satisfaction—other than the supreme satisfaction of breathing for and living through her only surviving son. She was neurasthenic, hypochondriac, an anxious, medically hysterical type; in practical affairs, penny-pinching and money-grubbing and, although the family possessed substantial resources, she was constantly preoccupied with the cost of everything and was niggardly in her dispensations. When her clothes wore out, she sold them. When she made a bad bargain, she reneged. The one exception to this was her marriage to Alphonse. Her romantic adolescent dream had vanished but the penance continued *in perpetuum*. She was a martyr to her marriage, a martyr to her son's ill health, broken legs, and long convalescences, and the modifications these imposed on her way of life. They did make it easier to avoid Alphonse, however, and the exquisite masochism of her Florence Nightingale role was only occasionally marred by a peevish revolt against the necessity of choosing one's vacation spots and limiting one's stays in accordance with Henri's doctors' recommendations.

Adèle's only other child died when Henri was four. After that the marriage was a dead letter and all her attentions were focussed on Henri. Adèle's brother married Alphonse's sister, and with them one child succeeded another; even writing off all the still-births and early deaths, they still reached number 14. How much this may have troubled Adèle is not easy to determine; nor can one quickly decide how much of her exasperating religiosity was due to inherited superstition and how much to sheer desperation. And it would take more study to know to what extent Alphonse's "eccentricities"—kite-flying, falconry, a penchant for outlandish costumes, and his compulsive year-around killing ("the incomparable sportsman")—were intensified by the behavior of this possessive, overprotective mother—Adèle—who was in no sense a wife.

Adèle pours out her heart to her "Mama" and can stay away from her only so long. In her letters she yearns to revert to the happier days of her childhood when Mama solved all her problems. Totally dependent herself, she clings to Henri in the classic reaction which unknowingly, pathetically, and ultimately tragically, could only have made him as helpless as she herself. "The tragic fall at Barèges"—Lautrec's second accident—which so many writers have seen as the decisive factor in his evolution, was, still, only an accident. The determinant was his heredity—and Adèle. Fortunately Lautrec's genius fought hard for expression, and he was able to break loose from "this sainted woman" and her deforming touch. But in his reaction against her life-denying, smothering embrace, he went as far as one could in the other direction. In his twenties she was still referring to him as "my little man." But by that time Henri was trying to prove to himself and to the world that he was *not* Mama's little man by launching himself on the road to alcoholism and by cohabiting with women who were polar opposites to Adèle and all she represented—a fauna that one of the family publicists has assured us was too unworthy a prize to have satisfied someone as "richly gifted and so completely refined" as Henri. Obviously. And yet the real reasons for Henri's dedication to such an unworthy and eventually fatal way of life have never been realistically explored.

Throughout the letters there are cameos of life in France under the Second Empire and Third Republic—political crises, fashion notes, involuntary social insights—but it is the character and weaknesses of Adèle and the pathetic nature of her emotional responses and conditioning that give them their special value. She omits nothing, she tells her stories straight, and her occasional successive versions of the same event written first to her mother and then to her mother-in-law often result in an even more enlightening diffraction phenomenon due to the changing audience. And she tells us much that no one else has ever told us by simply being herself. Thus there are two parallel sound tracks: her detailed recitals of the facts and the insistent, inescapable overtones provided by her nature and her reactions.

In the end, of course, the umbilical cord proves the strongest bond and Henri, broken, drunken, dragged himself back to die in his mother's arms at Malromé, sobbing with his last breath, "Mama, you, only you." At the beginning of his Montmartre life he wrote to his father's brother, Uncle Charles, who had encouraged his art studies from the first, ". . . I feel myself held back by a great load of sentimental considerations that I must absolutely forget if I wish to achieve anything." Just how great a load it must have been, this archive lets us see.

The original drawings, mostly in pencil, a few in ink or colored, include the earliest known drawings by Lautrec. It is generally recorded that he began to draw at the age of ten; some of these were done, demonstrably, when he was eight; some, indubitably, when he was six, and a few probably even earlier. Others, principally from among those of larger format in the album, are from his mid-teens. The most interesting aspect of the drawings is the fact that even the very earliest of them show the same sharp wit and intelligence that characterize Lautrec's mature work.

484. Bound sketchbook. Drawings from several periods, most of them very early, 35 pp. 9″ x 7″. There are sketches of animals—goats, monkeys, horses, dogs dressed as boys and wearing spurs, others bearing arms, a jackrabbit, waterfowl, and other birds—a costumed rider (probably Alphonse) on horseback or astride a large dog, representations of the devil, duelists, men in medieval and seventeenth-century costumes, the Château du Bosc, the family priest with the head of a dog smoking a pipe. Many of these drawings were done before Lautrec's accidents and they make clear that the commonly held thesis that his accidents turned him into an artist is little more than a romantic fabrication. These earliest drawings, however "childish" they may be from a technical standpoint, have a precocious self-assurance, along with the full flavor and incisive observation of his later work.

485. Album containing 11 loose sheets, most of which have drawings and sketches on both sides:

Le Souffle-au-cul (3 figures with self-portrait); sketches on verso. 5¼″ x 8½″.

The Cooks; sketches of judges on verso. 6⅞″ x 9″.

Sheet of sketches (dogs riding on horseback, fences, coach and pair, horses, etc.); heads, horses, and dogs on verso. 10½″ x 9¼″.

The Château du Bosc. 7″ x 9¼″.

Sheet of sketches (man with telescope, man with trumpet, bearded man, etc.). 5¼″ x 8½″.

Sheet of sketches (horseback riders, one probably his father, cormorants, train entering a tunnel, dog, horse, goat, etc.), signed "henri"; sketches, including monkeys and other animals in military costume carrying rifles, etc. on verso. 7″ x 9″.

Sheet of sketches (horses and other animals, cormorants, military figure); sketches on verso. 7″ x 9½″.

Sheet of sketches (five walking men, blind beggar with dog, head of bulldog; inscribed in Henri's hand *Bonne Fête*; study of elderly woman, dog, baby, and monkeys on verso. 9″ x 6⅞″.

Sheet of sketches (coachman on the box, horses, dog, walking figure), signed "henri"; animal studies on verso. 6⅞″ x 9″.

The Château du Bosc as a ship under sail, signed "Henri." 9¼″ x 7⅞″.

Sheet of sketches (3 ships), signed "Henri." 9⅞″ x 7⅞″.

Most of the subjects in both the sketchbook and the album were drawn from the family environment. For example, Henri was devoted to his cormorants, and the "study of elderly woman" is probably a sketch of his great-grandmother, who surrounded herself with monkeys and baboons. The cooks are the cooks at the Château du Bosc, and so on. A number of the people and sketches are referred to in the letters.

486. *Kyrie*. Watercolor. Measures 9⅞″ x 6⅜″. Inscribed with the brush, lower right, "1881 T-L. Kyrie," and, in pencil, below:

à Stern. T-Lautrec.

Painted by Lautrec ca. April 1881, at Nice, when he was 16½. Given by him to his lithographic printer, Stern, some years later, at which time he added the penciled inscription.

Among the letters in the family archives (no. 483) are these from Adèle, Comtesse de Toulouse-Lautrec, which place in context the painting of *Kyrie*:

Nice—Easter, 1881

Lent has gone: Father Félix has surely done a great deal of good by his fine words, so logical and so consoling: listening to him one loses sight of the sorrows of life since God alone and eternity are the goal—so beautiful and so near. Henry also has appreciated his sermons, *long* though they were and the seats so uncomfortable. He thinks only of painting, more than ever, and is making progress with his portrait sketches: that amuses the guests at the hotel and I may say also that his good nature makes everyone love him . . . .

Adèle to her mother-in-law.

Paris, 29 April, 1881

Alphonse reached Pérey's [Hotel] at the same time we did . . . . He is very busy with Henry, and Princeteau [Lautrec's painting teacher] is literally transported at the sight of [Henry's] masterpieces. Even less than that would have sufficed to transport my little man to seventh heaven and his Mama is happy to see him happy . . . .

Adèle to her mother.

TRISTAN TZARA

487. 15 holograph letters signed to Pierre Albert-Birot, 1917–1919. Some on the letterhead of the Mouvement Dada, Zurich. Tzara sends news of Dada activities in Zurich: a lecture with "projection-explosion," the Dada anthology, his own poems (*Boxe, Signe de l'Ile de Pâques, La Mort de Guillaume Apollinaire*), and his forthcoming book, *Cinéma calendrier du coeur abstrait*.

Discusses Yvan Goll, Janco, Arp, Picabia, and asks Albert-Birot to round up contributions for *Dada* from Aragon, Breton, Radiguet, Gabory, and other friends.

488. *Note 12 sur la poésie nègre*. Typescript signed, dated 1917. Folio. With annotations in red ink by Pierre Albert-Birot for its publication in *SIC*.

489. *Grains et issues.* Typescript with holograph corrections, 141 pp., of the book published in 1935 by Denoël et Steele. 4to. The first page bears the following inscription: "A Valentine [Hugo] avec l'expression de mon amitié entière. Tzara. 28 mars 1935."

The manuscript has a heavy brown paper wrapper covered on one side with a presentation drawing in blue and red crayon by Tzara.

490. *Parler seul.* Holograph manuscript signed, 15 pp. Folio. Inscribed: "Pour Jeanne Bonnafé / St. Alban / le 5 septembre / 1945 / Tristan Tzara."

Madame Bonnafé was the wife of the director of the psychiatric hospital of St.-Alban, where Tzara wrote these poems. This manuscript includes about two-thirds of the text of the folio volume published in 1950 under this title with original lithographs by Miró. It is accompanied by a handwritten (comic) dinner menu for the hospital, with decorations in colored crayons by Tzara.

For three months during the German occupation, Paul Éluard took refuge at this hospital and later wrote *Souvenirs de la maison des fous* (Paris: Éditions "Pro Francia," 1946) based on his stay there.

491. *Juste présent.* Holograph manuscript signed, dated 11 December 1947, 5 pp. and title page.

492. *Portrait de Tristan Tzara* by Valentine Hugo. India ink. 10⅝" x 8¼". Signed, upper right. A study for the 1920 portrait reproduced in the Larousse encyclopedia. Inscribed in blue ink, lower margin:

Capitaine! / Prends garde aux yeux bleus. / Tristan Tzara, 1920.

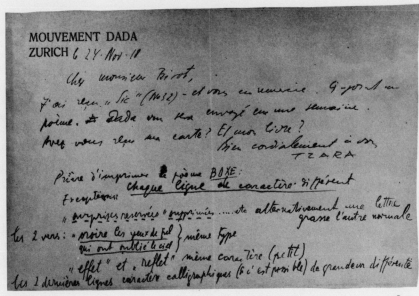

bg. d. de

Avec toi, je ne connais que des extrêmes. — Quel signe! quel symptôme!

Oui. quelques minutes de ma visite d'hier ont été de telle puissance tendresse — (et en toi aussi, il me semble), que j'en suis encore aussi fou et exaspéré d'idéale jonction et totale — et vitale que je puis l'être et l'étais — de fureur, d'amertume, de détresse et de jalousie —

Oui. mon semblable toi, mon amour. quel baiser is avons du échanger entre ces reprises d'écriture —! Et il a fallu (Ici — tout : ici, compris l'Artiste redevient en moi — Cela comp un tableau — une scène inouïe extraordinaire intensité. On le déchire, mais on le devoir. Deux violences entre quelques yeux et une telle résolution

493

Comment l'on se détruit pour ne pas savoir détruire une image — ou son pouvoir.

Et il n'est pas de plus irritant problème, car telle image paraît peu de chose, et son pouvoir se révèle sans nécessité. La liaison: Image → Pouvoir de d'action et de passion semble arbitraire, fortuite puisque le même image, en d'autres temps, ou dans d'autres êtres, n'a aucune force

L'association Idée — valeur est irrationnelle puisque l'idée par soi n'est pas homogène avec une valeur.

de plus, s'il est des associations de ce genre qui sont des acquisitions inévitables, faisant partie des fonctionnements normal — comme de la vue d'un mets à l'appétit, etc., — il en est d'autres toutes singulières.

Par ex. Il faut ici que l'idée de ..... se soit insérée dans le fonctionnement normal de Gz. Et c'est cela qui est .. anormal.

C'est l'histoire de toute intoxication.

493

493. Dossier of unpublished manuscript (part holograph, the rest typed by Valéry himself) covering the final years of Valéry's life and the play *Mon Faust*, which he had hoped to make the culmination of his life work, 175 pp.

In 1924 Valéry met a handsome young woman named Jeanne Loviton. She had recently been admitted to the Paris bar but was hoping to become a writer. Their attraction to each other was immediate, but two years later, Jeanne became engaged to marry a popular novelist and playwright, and broke off relations with Valéry. In 1935, divorced and now writing under the name Jeanne Larivière and soon thereafter Jean Voilier, she renewed her friendship with Valéry and from that moment on, became his close companion. Valéry saw in her an exceptional combination of physical beauty and intellectual grace and came to look upon her as, potentially, the successor to Colette. He spent more and more time in her company and before long was ecstatically in love with her. Their affair continued through the war years, brightening Valéry's life, stimulating his creative processes, and gradually becoming the most important, indeed indispensable, element in the elaboration of what he hoped would prove to be his greatest achievement (". . . this great work in my head, which will finally rid me entirely of myself. . . .").

"This great work" was Valéry's treatment of the Faust legend, with which he had become increasingly preoccupied. One day in 1940, as Valéry later wrote, "I found myself talking to myself with two voices and I began to write down what came forth." What came forth, in the months that followed, were parts of two plays on the Faust theme. One of them became a well-developed but incomplete three-act comedy lacking only the dénouement of a fourth act to make it a brilliant and original contemporary version of the theme. Valéry called it *Lust, la demoiselle de cristal*. The other, a shorter, less dramatic work, about two-thirds complete, Valéry called a *féerie dramatique*, and entitled *Le Solitaire ou les malédictions d'univers*. It was his aim, he tells us, to create a third *Faust* made up of a variety of dramatic forms: comedy and tragedy, to fit the occasion; prose and verse, according to the mood.

The role of Lust, Faust's secretary in the first work, was obviously built around Jean Voilier (who appears elsewhere in his work under the names Héra, Rachel, and Calypso). The character of Faust is quite clearly identified in the author's mind (and treatment) with Valéry himself. And the relationship between the two—although it is never resolved and in the end becomes somewhat ambiguous and confused—is based on Valéry's concept of his formative role in the development of Lust's flesh-and-blood prototype from a repository of unrealized virtualities to the perfect female expression of *coeur-esprit* which he had visualized.

Just as their friendship provided the basis of *Mon Faust*, it resulted in other forms of collaboration as well: Héra brought out an occasional Valéry paper in a publishing firm she had inherited from her father; Valéry illustrated a limited edition of a book she had written, *Ville Ouverte*. Most important, Valéry often acknowledged in himself a fresh and vigorous poetic surge that he had not always felt since his investiture as the leading literary lion of pre-war Paris.

Je t'aime, mon travail, quand tu es
véritablement le mien — toi que je
reconnais sous toutes les formes — toi seul,
en somme, es vraiment moi. Que je maîtrise
le système vivant des nerfs de xeimeas
ou des puissances pensantes de x —
que je me sente pénétrant entre mes
durées par le plus rapide —

Je ne possède si tu me possèdes, je
suis maître si je suis ton esclave et ton
instrument —

comme le corps du cavalier monté par
son idée et son énergie monte le bête et
se fait un seul être avec elle —

Comme la barque entre le havre et la
toile, contre le vent par le vent —

Obéis ne te laisse pas emporter (comme tant le
((libèrent)) par la seule force qui n'est pas tienne
et

Faust en tentation intellectuelle

Lust arrive.

Taisez-vous ne dites rien.
Mais il faut que je vous parle, l'amour
mon cœur... donner encore plus de
valeur que ce que tu as fait
montre que j'ai si tu es pas

à iia   En vain tu t'en croyais et
tu te trompes en

Et la   Et pendant
Tu ne réfléchis à rien qu'à tes
affaires, arrangements, que tu combines
1) Bonheur — mariage — avenir — constructions
(affaires, aménagements, toilettes, bibelots — Gelotk,
... toute ta vie — Relations
2) Roman — Filles — Sujets...
un certain goût de gloire —

Discours ne sont
pas utiles
la longue — ont rendu riches ni
l'avais je n'ai jamais
ni malheur

Héra did indeed have literary ambitions but she was a creature of luxury, and her way of life was very important to her. She had an elegant town house with a secluded garden in the heart of Paris, and she was restoring a Renaissance château in the center of France. In these places Valéry found release from the social and paraliterary distractions of his increasingly fragmented life. But her life-style required money and Héra became more and more involved with the problems that requirement raised. In the pursuit of her business interests she became friendly with a well-known publisher—Robert Denoël—a man much nearer her own age. They worked out plans to associate their two firms and in the process fell in love and decided to marry. On Easter Sunday in 1944 Héra went to Valéry, told him her plans and, wanting to be both loyal and generous, said that there would be no change in her feeling for or relationship with him. She was a practical woman, but Valéry was in love as he had never been before. He had made his peace with the fact that she was also the friend of Jean Giraudoux and Saint-John Perse, but *this* declaration, with all it portended for the future, was too much, and the sky fell in on him.

He tried to bear up under the shock. He filled one of the spiral-bound notebooks he habitually used with the story (in two parallel texts) of his meeting with Héra (or Xiemeas, as she is sometimes referred to here). The notebook also contains passages concerning Wagner, Gide, Maurice Sachs, and Fargue, a text for the fourth act of *Mon Faust*, and brief passages which Valéry intended for an uncompleted collection, *Alphabet*, and for *Stratonice*, a play on which he had meditated for many years. But he keeps coming back to Héra and her infidelity. Some of these passages are in Italian, Latin, or Greek; a few, in a cryptic private language.

In the course of Valéry's account of his meeting with Xiemeas there is a remarkable analysis of the process of affective involvement. And beginning on page 26 of Act I of the published version of *Mon Faust*, this philosophical analysis is translated into dramatic action—a classic example of Valéry's method of working: a personal experience is recorded, analyzed, reduced to its philosophical and at times almost abstract components, and stored in the notebook. Later it is reworked and adapted to the literary exercise currently in hand.

In the year that follows, Valéry comes to grips, outside the notebook, with the effects of Héra's "betrayal" on his life and work. In a continuing private journal, he sets down a series of letters to himself and to her, and in poems inspired by a wide range of emotions, he appraises his present condition, human and creative. Each morning before daybreak he sits down at his table to write, just as he has done all his working life. And now, as he surveys the wreckage, he tries to rationalize his fate on the basis of his past behavior and decides he is being tortured by one of the Furies, and that Héra, too, will receive her punishment one day.

When the paroxysms subside, Valéry is rational, at times passionately lyrical. There are occasional moments when he can write with a wry humor. But as the mood turns darker, he becomes jealous, vindictive, self-absorbed, and desperate. Often these pages are poignant and moving. At times they become as raw and intolerably painful as the wounds and spasms that produced them. And yet, in spite of this, time and again the creative process advances a step beyond the confession, the recital, or the dramatization, to an apparently involuntary (or at least conditioned) refinement of the facts. One day they appear *so*; the next day they are approached from a different vantage point and are metamorphosed into a quite different result: from the personal to the universal, from private pain to a near-serenity achieved through the ordering of art.

There are occasional reunions, whose extremes of emotion leave Valéry increasingly shaken. Often his *cris de coeur* take the form of prose poems, now short, now very long. At other times the form is what he refers to as "quasi-poèmes." On occasion his voice rises in a way no earlier work of his had prepared us for. Then, suddenly, the language becomes terser, more disciplined. Later, and in contrast to the freedom of the "quasi-poèmes," he turns to more rigorous metrical forms and produces some magnificent poems of traditional structure.

During these months of self-torture and self-examination, Valéry tries to work on other things—a long philosophical analysis of law and a review of a major work on memory. He begins to write *Mes Mémoires*, but doesn't get far beyond the title. At other times he loses his memory. When it returns, it brings with it dreams of childhood fantasies.

Throughout, there is the insistent need to finish *Mon Faust*. But he is at the end of his strength from unrelieved insomnia. He has new ideas for Act IV that reinforce those vague ideas he had earlier. He analyzes the metaphysics of the problem in terms which are conceptually extraordinary but practically—for him, now—unrealizable.

In the course of a ten-page letter, Valéry traces the history of his hopes to model Héra into an incomparable being, "a work which could not be and which must remain as illusory as a certain fourth act . . . and so many other things." One of those other things was to have been a book called *Inferno*. Its early notations and analyses are set down in a schoolboy's notebook. They relate in equal measure to the catastrophe and to *Mon Faust* (". . . how one destroys oneself through not knowing how to destroy an image or its power . . . .").

The last page of the dossier is the sheet on which, on 25 May 1945, Valéry set down a last, clear-eyed statement of his view of his role as a writer. Six days later he was confined to his bed and on 20 July he died. On the 24th his coffin was carried by uniformed guards, in a torchlight procession to the rhythm of muffled drums, from the Place Victor-Hugo to the Trocadéro. It was placed on a catafalque, which had been draped with the tricolor and set up between the two wings of the Palais de Chaillot, on whose façade are engraved four brief texts by Valéry. Across the Seine the Panthéon was illuminated. All the rest of Paris was in darkness. Throughout the night, students kept watch as crowds filed past the bier. In the morning, General De Gaulle presided over the official ceremony and military honors that preceded the convoy's departure for Sète and the burial in the Cimetière Saint-Charles, Valéry's *Cimetière Marin*.

The pomp and ceremony with which France paid its final respects to its most eminent man of letters underline the pathos of the bitter epitaph he had written for himself:

> I finish this life in vulgarity, a ridiculous victim in my own eyes, after having believed I would finish it in a twilight of love absolute and incorruptible and of spiritual power recognized by all as rigorously and justly acquired.

494. *Études pour "Mon Faust." Illustrations de l'auteur interprétées en gravure sur bois par Pierre Bouchet.* [Paris] Les Cent-Une, 1941. 4to, full morocco, raised bands, top edges gilt, inner gilt dentelles, original wrappers bound in, uncut.

First edition. Privately printed in an edition of 101 numbered copies for Les Cent-Une, Société de Femmes Bibliophiles. Printed on the hand press of Pierre Bouchet on *vélin d'Arches* with the watermark of the Cent-Une.

495. *"Mon Faust." I. Lust ou La Demoiselle de Cristal. Comédie. II. Le Solitaire ou Les Malédictions d'Univers. Féerie dramatique.* [Paris] Gallimard [1945]. 4to, loose in sheets within original wrappers, uncut, in slipcase.

First printing of the definitive text. Limited to 120 numbered copies printed in two colors on *Mûrier d'Annam* by Féquet et Baudier. This edition contains the third act, not included in the 1941 edition. At the end of Act III is a sheet imprinted, "Fourth and Final Act. Missing."

496. *Cantate du Narcisse.* [Paris] Les Centraux Bibliophiles, 1956. Illustrated by Hans Erni with 25 original lithographs. Folio, loose in sheets, within original wrappers, uncut, and decorative board case.

The book is dedicated *A Jean Voilier*. This edition, limited to 141 copies, was designed by Maurice Darantière. Proof copy, *hors série*, printed on blue paper with added suites on black, blue, white, and Japan papers. Laid in are two letters from Hans Erni to Darantière concerning the book, each of which has an original pen-and-ink drawing by the artist; also laid in is a copy of the menu for the dinner celebrating the book's publication.

497. *Ville Ouverte*, by Jean Voilier. Paris: Éditions Émile-Paul Frères, 1942. Illustrated by Paul Valéry with original lithographs. Small folio, original wrappers, uncut.

One of 30 large-paper copies on *papier Vidalon*, with an added suite, on China paper, of Valéry's lithographs, including a number of unpublished states. With the Daragnès bookplate. The book is dedicated *A Paul Valéry / dont ce texte a tenté le crayon, / bien amicalement / J.V.*

498. 13 holograph letters signed to John Middleton Murry, 1917–1936, 41 pp. An outstanding correspondence that began with Middleton Murry's review of *La Jeune Parque* in the *Times*. In it Valéry sets forth some of his most personal feelings about poetry in general, about his own work—past, present, and future—and about other writers who interest him particularly, including Baudelaire, Poe, and Gide. A few excerpts:

Between 1893 and 1913 I left poetry alone. I have never looked on myself as a poet and I still believe that I am not essentially a poet. I have only sought a form of personal analysis and personal combinations of my possibilities. . . .

From 1893 to 1913, I spent what time my occupations left me in research of a logical and psychological nature, and I thought no more about the art of poetry. . . . In 1913, my friends at the *Nouvelle Revue Française* insisted on publishing a collection of my early verse; that collection seemed to me so slender that I decided to add about thirty more lines. Those thirty obliged me to write five-hundred. . . . You have sensed perfectly the essential role of the intellectual element in *La Jeune Parque* and the sustained role of the musical element. . . . For me, the idea of "Awareness" ["*Conscience*"] has a primary role in literary creation. I would rather do a book that was unsuccessful but done consciously than write a masterpiece by chance. . . . At this moment poetry just doesn't interest me. I give myself over to it by fits . . . widely separated. The latest one, which I have just come out of, has tired me greatly. . . . In rereading Poe . . . I felt a certain disappointment with *Eureka*, which had seemed so admirable to me when I was young. . . . But what an influence on literature Poe has had! He created three or four genres. And I consider that he is the source, in France, of that transformation of poetry that has brought about the concept of *la poésie pure*. . . . If I were to tell you that literature is not my principal goal, that I write only to keep in trim, not for love, I'm afraid you would accuse me of a particular kind of charlatanism, and yet that is the truth. . . .

499. Holograph manuscript and typescript (typed by Valéry), 16 pp. Notes for a paper on history.

500. *Earlier Visits to England.* Typescript signed, 10 pp. Folio. Title in English, but text in French, typed by Valéry and with holograph corrections in his hand.

Reminiscences of a trip to England in 1894, during which he talked with Aubrey Beardsley about Toulouse-Lautrec, with Edmund Gosse about Mallarmé and, armed with a letter of introduction from Marcel Schwob, visited George Meredith at Box Hill.

501. *Introduction à la méthode de Léonard de Vinci.* Paris: Éditions de la Nouvelle Revue Française (1919). 4to, original wrappers, uncut and unopened. First book publication. One of 128 numbered large-paper copies on *Lafuma.*

Leonardo's creativity had fascinated Valéry ever since his youth. In 1894 Juliette Adam asked him for an article dealing with the question for *La Nouvelle Revue.* As the article took form, Valéry wrote to his brother Jules (in December 1894), ". . . They say that his was a *universal* mind. What is the meaning . . . the force of that proposition? Can one be universal? Is there a method by which one can become universal?"

502. *Introduction to the Method of Leonardo da Vinci translated from the French of Paul Valéry of the académie française by Thomas McGreevy.* London: John Rodker, 1929. Small folio, original green-vellum-backed decorative

boards. From the library of James Joyce, with his ownership stamp on the inside back cover.

One of 50 specially bound copies, printed on hand-made paper and signed by the author and the translator (Copy No. 45). The total edition was limited to 875.

503. 2 holograph letters signed to François Mauriac, one dated "17 mai 1920," 8 pp. Valéry has written critically of Pascal, and Mauriac has devoted an article to Pascal's defense; Valéry returns to the attack, this time stressing the bad faith of Pascal's apologetics. In the second letter, he attempts to comfort Mauriac by interpreting another writer as having placed Mauriac in the company of Baudelaire, Dostoevski, and Gide.

504. Holograph letter (draft) [to Jean de La Tour, 28 July 1933], 4 pp. Valéry attempts to define his philosophical position as a writer.

505. Holograph letter signed [to Paul Souday], 1 September 1922, 3 pp. Thanks Souday for his review of *Charmes* and reaffirms his gratitude for the generous and courageous support Souday gave to *La Jeune Parque*.

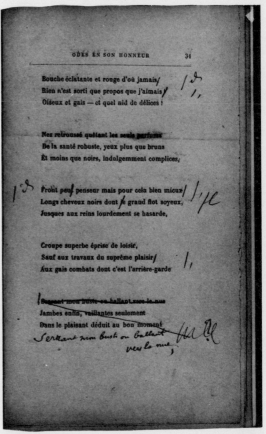

506. Holograph letter signed to Natalie Clifford Barney [1918], 2 pp. Thanks her for her "perfumed note" and for her translation of *Monsieur Teste*, which he has read in *The Dial*.

507. Holograph letter signed from T. S. Eliot to G. Jean-Aubry, 1 November 1922, 2 pp. In French. Regrets his delay in returning and his inability to be at Lady Colfax's to see Valéry, "France's greatest poet." Charles Whibley, too, wanted to see Valéry. Eliot will have an issue of *The Criterion* sent to Jean-Aubry.

508. 7 photographs, 2 inscribed.

PAUL VERLAINE

509. *Les Poètes maudits. Tristan Corbière. Arthur Rimbaud. Stéphane Mallarmé.* Paris: Léon Vanier, 1884. 12mo, full crimson morocco, raised bands, all edges gilt, inner gilt dentelles, original wrappers bound in, uncut, slipcase (binding by Semet & Plumelle).

> The rare first edition, limited to 253 copies. Contains the first printing of six major poems of Rimbaud: *Voyelles, Oraison du soir, Les Assis, Les Effarés, Les Chercheuses de poux,* and *Le Bateau ivre.*
> Verlaine's first prose work and his first book to be published by Vanier. He now had, for the first time, a publisher willing to bring out his books at the publisher's expense and to pay him royalties on them.

510. *Les Poètes maudits. Nouvelle édition ornée de six portraits par Luque. Tristan Corbière, Arthur Rimbaud, Stéphane Mallarmé, Marceline Desbordes-Valmore, Villiers de l'Isle-Adam, Pauvre Lélian.* Paris: Léon Vanier, 1888. 12mo, contemporary half-morocco, raised bands, with gilt-stamped fleurs-de-lis on backstrip.

> First edition for the chapters devoted to Desbordes-Valmore, Villiers, and Verlaine (Pauvre Lélian). Two poems of Rimbaud appear here for the first time: *Le Coeur volé* and *Tête de faune*. Edition limited to 600 copies.

511. *Odes en son honneur.* Paris: Léon Vanier, 1893. 12mo, three-quarter crushed levant, raised bands, top edges gilt, original wrappers bound in, uncut (binding by Vermorel). First edition. One of Verlaine's own favorites among his books.

512. *Odes en son honneur.* 12mo, three-quarter blue crushed levant, top edges gilt (binding by Stroobants). From the library of Descamps-Scrive, with the bookplate.

> This is a bound set of page proofs, corrected throughout by Verlaine. The stamps of the printer—Charles Hérissey, Evreux—on the various segments of the proofs are dated 26, 28, and 30 November 1892. The book was published on 6 May 1893.

184

513. *Odes en son honneur.* Holograph manuscripts of 4 poems from this book:

    No. V—*"Quand je cause avec toi paisiblement. . . ."*

    No. X—*Et maintenant, aux Fesses!* (latter portion).

    No. XI—*Riche ventre qui n'a jamais porté.*

    No. XIV—*Nous sommes bien faits l'un pour l'autre.*

514. *Portrait de Paul Verlaine* by F.-A. Cazals. Oil on canvas. Measures 21" x 14½". Verlaine is shown in left profile, wearing a blue jacket and with a red scarf around his neck. Cazals and Verlaine were close friends in Verlaine's late years.

515. *Paul Verlaine* by Maurice Baud. Wood engraving, ca. 1887, from a drawing by David Estoppey. Published in Ch. Morice's *Paul Verlaine* (1888).

    Trial proof with wide margins, on *Japon impérial.* Measures 13⅜" x 8⅝". Inscribed by Baud to Verlaine's publisher, Léon Vanier, and with identifying notes below in Vanier's hand.

516. *Verlaine. Avril 1884, Café du Globe* by Ferdinand Bac. Pencil, with touches of color. Measures 9 3-16" x 3 3-16". Signed, lower right.

517. *Paul Verlaine au Café François Ier.* Photograph signed "Dornac." Measures 4⅜" x 6½". This photograph, in its present frame, hung on the wall next to Adrienne Monnier's desk in her bookshop, La Maison des Amis des Livres, until her death.

518. *Axël*. Paris: Quantin, 1890. 8vo, three-quarter blue crushed levant, original wrappers bound in, completely untrimmed (binding by Stroobants). First edition of the play on which Villiers worked during most of his life: his spiritual testament and the quintessential Symbolist drama.

Villiers was going over the proofs of *Axël* during his last illness, and the book appeared only after his death. This copy bears a presentation inscription in the hand of Stéphane Mallarmé, signed by Mallarmé and J.-K. Huysmans, Villiers's executors. It is inscribed to "Monsieur Edmond Fournier, one of Villiers's last visitors."

Fournier was the doctor of Méry Laurent, who had sent him to look after Villiers in his last days in the absence of Villiers's own doctors, Albert Robin and Henri Cazalis. Dr. Fournier and his brother, Professor Alfred Fournier, were distinguished bibliophiles whose outstanding library was dispersed in a sale held at the Hôtel Drouot in Paris from 14 to 18 June 1926. Dr. Fournier's small printed book ticket with his inventory number is inside the front cover. The book contains the following autograph material:

> Holograph letter signed from Villiers to Méry Laurent, 10 February 1889, 2 pp. Villiers is up and about but still in no position to make sparkling conversation. "I have come to understand the curious fact . . . that the best policy is not to worry about anything any more . . . simply to stay happy, come what may. . . ." (Méry Laurent—Marie-Rose Laurent, née Louviot—was a plump, blond, music-hall artiste who first came to public attention in a Venus-on-the-half-shell tableau at the Châtelet Theatre. After that her rise was rapid. She became the mistress of a transplanted Philadelphian, Thomas W. Evans, who was personal dentist to Napoléon III and whose friendship with the Emperor had made him a rich man. Evans was not only rich but broad-minded as well, and he approved of Méry Laurent's liaisons with the painters and poets attracted by her opulent charms. Villiers was her devoted friend. Manet, too, was greatly taken by her beauty, and made many drawings and paintings of her.
>
> Through Manet, Méry Laurent met Mallarmé and was fascinated by his wit, his voice, and his gracious manner. After Manet's death, in 1883, Méry Laurent was briefly linked with François Coppée and soon after that became Mallarmé's mistress. Later, Proust used traces of her in creating the character Odette de Crécy.

Holograph letter signed from Villiers to Mallarmé, with Villiers's name written in pencil in Mallarmé's hand on verso. Villiers has worked all night, until 6:30 in the morning and can hardly see to write this letter. "On Tuesday evening I will come to ask you . . . what you think about my *Carmélite*. . . ." He asks Mallarmé to address his letters in care of Mme. Gaillard (the mother of Nina de Villard, Villiers's mistress), where he goes every evening.

Holograph letter signed "Méry," 2 pp. Concerning a soirée which Mallarmé will attend with his family.

Holograph manuscript signed by Remy de Gourmont, 3 pp. On the first performance of *Axël* (26 February 1894). Some have protested the shortened version of the play, but Gourmont approves of the cuts and is certain Villiers would have approved also. In Germany they are currently playing *Faust* with cuts (and still not enough of them, in the opinion of some). This production of *Axël* will give a wide public the opportunity to acquaint itself with "a masterpiece of thought and style and to render an important practical service to the young son of a great writer. . . ."

Yeats went over to Paris from Dublin in February 1894 and, with Maud Gonne, attended that first performance. In an article he published in the April issue of the *Bookman*, he placed parts of *Axël* ("lines of the adept Janus, of the Medusa Sara") close to some of the "perfect things" in the "hierarchy of those recollections which are our standards and our beacons." Over the next few years, the impact of the play became increasingly evident in Yeats's work (e.g., *The Wind Among the Reeds*), and in the work of all writers rebelling against what Yeats referred to as "the photographing of life," in an effort to return "by the path of symbolism to imagination and poetry, the only things which are ever permanent."

(L.D.)   Delteil, Loÿs. *Le Peintre-Graveur Illustré. Tome Dix-septième. Camille Pissarro, Auguste Renoir, Alfred Sisley.* Paris, 1923.

(Guérin)   Guérin, Marcel. *L'Oeuvre gravé de Gauguin.* 2 vols. Paris: Floury, 1927.

(Johnson)   Johnson, Una E. *Ambroise Vollard Éditeur. 1867–1939. An Appreciation and Catalogue.* New York: Wittenborn and Company, 1944.

(Mellerio)   Mellerio, André. *Odilon Redon. Avec une gravure originale de l'artiste.* [Paris] Société pour l'Étude de la Gravure Française, 1913.

(Skira)   Skira, Albert. *Anthologie du Livre Illustré par les peintres et sculpteurs de l'École de Paris . . . Catalogue établi par Albert Skira.* Genève: Éditions Albert Skira [1946].

(Terrasse)   Terrasse, Charles. *Bonnard.* Paris: Floury, 1927.

(Venturi)   Venturi, Lionello. *Cézanne. Son art—son oeuvre.* 2 vols. Paris: Paul Rosenberg, 1936.

(Zervos)   Zervos, Christian. *Pablo Picasso par Christian Zervos. Vol. 1. Oeuvres de 1895 à 1906.* Paris: Éditions "Cahiers d'Art," 1951.

"A Francis Poulenc" 75
"A Guillaume Apollinaire, mon ami" 17
"A la musique" 149
"A propos de l'inutilité du théâtre au théâ-
    tre" 98
A la recherche d'André Gide 84
A la recherche du temps perdu 130
A La Sirène. See "Éditions de la Sirène."
A l'ombre des jeunes filles en fleurs 130
"A propos de la nouvelle édition des Oeuvres
    de Rimbaud" 143
A une sérénité crispée 51
Abbaye de St.-Wandrille 69
Abécédaire des filles et de l'enfant chéri 121
Absent, L' 32
Académie Française 182
"Acte terrestre" 95
Adam 15
Adam, Juliette 182
"Additions à la bibliographie" 157
Adler, Rose 141, 142
"Affaires impersonnelles" 116
Afrique fantôme, L' 102
African sculpture 10
Age d'or, L' 51
Age de raison, L' 161
Agoult, Comtesse d' 104
Albaret, Céleste 134
Albert-Birot, Germaine, 12, 13, 14
Albert-Birot, Pierre 3, 7, 9, 12, 13, 14, 17,
    19, 120, 141, 174
Albin, Pierre 145
Albin-Guillot, Laure 69
Album des Peintres-Graveurs 51
Alfred Jarry ou le surmâle de lettres 98
"Alfred Stevens" 134

Alix, Mme. 54, 134
Alliance Typographique (M.-J. Poot et Com-
    pagnie) 141
Almanach du Père Ubu, illustré (1899), L' 98
Almanach surréaliste du demi-siècle 39
Alphabet (Auric) 135
"Alphabet" (Valéry) 179
"Amazon" 91
American Hospital in Paris 151
Amis de Redon, Les 139
"Amitié du prince" 155
Amour Fou, L' 37
Amours de deux bêtes, Les 24
Anabase 54
"Ancienne à la coiffe innombrable, L'" 157
André-Messager, Jean 69
Anouilh, Jean 9
Anthony, Susan B. 4
"Anti. . ., Les" 91
Aphrodite 108
Apollinaire, Guillaume 3, 7, 9–10, 12–17, 19,
    36, 40, 53, 72, 75, 91, 112, 122, 123, 125,
    129, 130, 141
Appel des canotiers du Taï aux hôtes de Ca-
    maret 158
Après-midi d'un faune, L' 111–112
"Après moi le sommeil" 75
Aragon, Louis 7, 19, 36, 37, 40, 120, 122,
    159, 174
Arbalète, L' 82
Arcane 17 37
Arche, L' 37, 88
Arkel 66
Arland, Marcel 36, 40, 122
Armistice 36, 75
Arp, Jean (Hans) 36, 92, 174

Artaud, Antonin 4, 20, 40, 122
Arthème Fayard et Cie. 60
"Arthur Rimbaud" 148
Arthur Rimbaud in London 143
Arthur Rimbaud. A Douai et à Charleville. Lettres et écrits inédits. Commentés par Georges Izambard 150
Artiste et son temps, L' 42
Artiste, L' 119
"Aseptique noyade pour amateurs programmatiques" 120
Asselineau, Charles 28
"Assis, Les" 184
Assommoir, L' 91
Astarté 106
Astruc, Gabriel 69, 137
Atlantic-Little, Brown 105
"Au lendemain des *Mamelles de Tirésias*" 14
Au Sans Pareil 37, 46, 122
Aubert, Georges 154
Audiberti, Jacques 20
Auric, Georges 20, 23–24, 57, 60, 88, 120, 135, 137, 162
Autobiography of Alice B. Toklas, The 124, 125
"Automatisme de la variante" 37
Automne, L' 151
Aux Lumières de Paris 122
"Avenir de la poésie" 75
"Awareness" 182
Axël 186–187
Aymé, Marcel 116

Bac, Ferdinand 185
Baiser du faune, Le 149
"Baiser du faune, Le," 149
Balcon, Le 108
Ballets Russes 14, 59, 69
Ballets sans musique, sans personne, sans rien 45
Ballets Suédois 162
Balzac, Honoré de 24, 158
Balzac 150
Banville, Théodore de 28, 111
Baobab 155
Bar Nicanor 119, 120
Barbezat, Marc 82
Bardey, Alfred 145
Bardey, Pierre 145
Barney, Natalie Clifford 91, 108, 184
Barrault, Jean-Louis 84
Basket 125, 127

Bataille, Georges 27, 32
"Bateau ivre, Le" 184
Bateau-Lavoir 124, 125
Baud, Maurice 185
Baudelaire 159
Baudelaire, Charles 3, 7n, 14n, 27, 27n, 28–29, 63, 79, 80, 91, 108, 115, 116, 144, 158, 159, 181, 183
Bauër, Henry 96, 112
Baudelaire-Dufaÿs 27
Bayntun 10
Beach, Sylvia 13, 76, 79
Beardsley, Aubrey 182
Beaumarchais, Pierre Augustin Caron de 14
Beauregard quarter 46
"Beauté sera convulsive ou ne sera pas, La" 37
Beauvoir, Simone de 32, 161
Beaux-Arts, Les 148
Bécat, Paul-Émile 79
Beckett, Samuel 4, 32–33
Bédier, Joseph 119
Before the Flowers of Friendship Faded Friendship Faded 165, 167
Bellmer, Hans 27, 36
Belle Enfant ou l'Amour à Quarante Ans, La 72
Benda, Julien 84
Benvenuto Cellini 34
Bérard, Christian 92, 167
"Berceau de Gertrude Stein ou Le Mystère de la Rue de Fleurus, Le" 92
"Berceuse" 155
Berl, Emmanuel 116
Berlioz, Hector 34
Bernard, Émile 79
Bernard, Mme. Louise 104
Bernard, M. 69
Bernier, Jean 40
Berrichon, Paterne 142–144, 145–146, 148
Berry, Walter 59
Berthelot, Philippe 146
Bertrand, Aloysius 79
Besnard, Albert 111, 112
Besnard, Annie 20
Bestiaire ou Cortège d'Orphée, Le 72
Bible d'Amiens, La 130
Bibliothèque de l'Occident 54, 55
Bibliothèque des Curieux 10, 16
Bibliothèque Littéraire Jacques Doucet 119
Bibliothèque Nationale 46, 130
Bibliothèque Spoelberch de Louvenjoul 119

Bienfeld [sic] 145
Billon, Pierre 154
Billy, Robert de 130
"Birthday Book, A" 127
Blaizot, A. 29
Blanche, Jacques-Émile 130
Blanchot, Maurice 32
Blin, Roger 32
Bloch, Camille 84
Bollori, Michel 87
Bonabel, Éliane 45
Boni, Albert & Charles 166
Bonjean, Jacques 58
Bonnafé, Jeanne 175
Bonnard, Pierre 35, 140
Bonnat, Léon 169
Bookman 187
Borelli, Jules 145
Börlin, Jean 162
Bosquet, Alain 157
Bossuet, Jacques Bénigne 101
Böttiger, Karl August 119
Bottini, Georges 76
Bouchet, Pierre 181
"Boucle retrouvée, La" 53
Boule de gui, La 72
Boully, Mouny de 116
Bourdelle, Émile-Antoine 151
Bourlinguer 46
Bousquet, Joë 36–37, 40, 100, 122, 161
Bouvard et Pécuchet 3
Box Hill 182
"Boxe" 174
Braque, Georges 10, 14, 122, 124n, 125
Brassaï 115
Bresson, Robert 154
Breton, André 7, 19, 36, 37, 39–40, 75, 96, 120, 122, 127, 157, 174
Brianchon, Maurice 88
Bubu de Montparnasse 72
Bülow, Hans von 104
Burty, Philippe 29
Bussy, Dorothy 84
Bussy, Simon 84
Butler, Samuel 101
Butor, Michel 41
Byron 127

Ça Ira 120
Cabaret artistique des Quat'zarts 97
Cabaret de la belle femme, Le 72
Cabaret du Clou 63

Cactriane 24
Café du Dôme 161
Café Riche 66
Cahiers d'Art 37, 127
Cahiers du Sud, Les 76
Calder, Alexander 41
"Calendrier éclair" 52
"Calendrier tour du monde des inventions tolérables" 39
Caligula 42
Callery, Mary 69
"calligramme" 7
Calligrammes 16
Calypso. *See* Voilier, Jean.
Camus, Albert 40, 42, 84
Canape 96
Cantate du Narcisse 181
Cap de bonne espérance, Le 19
Carayon 27
"Carmélite" 186
"Carnaval" 135
Carré, Albert 65, 66
Carrière, Eugène 112
Casadesus, Robert 137
Caves du Vatican, Les 84
Cazalis, Henri 112, 186
Cazals, F. -A. 98, 185
Céline, Louis-Ferdinand 3, 42, 44–45
Céline, Mme. Louis-Ferdinand 45
Cellini, Benvenuto 34
Cendrars, Blaise 3, 7, 17, 46, 57
Cent-Une, Les (Société de Femmes Bibliophiles) 181
Centraux Bibliophiles, Les 181
Cercle de la Librairie 13
César Antéchrist 95
"Cette année-là comme les autres nous avions besoin de contes" 76
Cézanne, Paul 46, 49, 51, 79, 164
Cézanne, Paul, *fils* 46, 49
Cézanne, Mme. Renée (Rivière) 139
Cézanne family 49
Chantiers 36
Chaperont, M. 151
Chapitres tournés en tous sens 164
Chagall, Marc 15, 122
Chamfort, Sébastien Roch Nicolas 42
"Chamfort" 42
Chansons de Bilitis 63, 65
Chapeau épinglé (La Fille de Berthe Morisot et sa cousine), Le 140
Char, René 36, 51, 53

Charles Baudelaire intime. Le Poète vierge 28, 29

Charlus, Baron de 134

Charmes 183

"Charogne, La" 29

Charpentier 51, 91

"Chasse spirituelle, La" 144

Château du Bosc 173

Chateaubriand, François René, Vicomte de 88

Chaucer, Geoffrey 3

Chausson, Ernest 54

Chemins de la liberté, Les 161

"Chercheuses de poux, Les" 149, 184

Chéri 60

"Cheveux gris, quand jeunesse les porte, Les" 57

"Chevelure, La" 65

"Chinois, Le" 164

Chirico, Giorgio de 16

Chopin, Frédéric 63, 104

"Christian Bérard et Pavel Tchelitchef" 92

Cimetière Marin 180

Cimetière Saint-Charles 180

Cinéma calendrier du coeur abstrait 174

Cinéastes-Bibliophiles, Les 81

Cinq grandes odes suivies d'un processionnal pour saluer le siècle nouveau 54–55

Cinq poèmes de Baudelaire 63

Circe episode 76

Cirque de l'Étoile Filante 151

Clarté 40

Clair, René 162

Claude Debussy 69

Claudel, Paul 54, 116, 142, 146

Claudel, Mme. Paul 146

Claudine 63

Clément, J. 113

Clichy prison 29

Cliquet-Pleyel, Henri 164

Cocteau, Mme. E. 60

Cocteau, Jean 7, 19, 20, 23, 24, 36, 57–60, 82–83, 84, 112, 116, 120, 129, 134, 135, 161, 162, 164

Cocteau, Paul 82

"coeur-esprit" 177

"Coeur volé, Le" 184

Colette, Sidonie Gabrielle Claudine 9, 23, 60–61, 63, 72, 177

Colfax, Lady 184

Collège de Charleville 148

Collier de griffes, Le 53

Collière, Marcel 97

Coligny-Châtillon, Louise, Comtesse de 16

Comédie-Française 16, 20

"Comment j'ai fait mes livres" 115

Communism 40, 84

Communist party 88

Communist propaganda 159

Concerto pour piano et orchestre 137

Concile féerique, Le 100

Condition humaine, La 113

Confession d'un enfant du siècle 57

Confessions 91

Connaissance du soir, La 37

Conquérants, Les 113

"Conscience" 182

Conservatoire (Paris) 54

Conservatoire Renée Maubel 13

Constant, Benjamin 42

Contact Editions 166

Coppée, François 112, 186

Coq et l'arlequin, Le 57

Corbière, Tristan 184

Cormon 169

Corneille, Pierre 107

Cornet à dés, Le 95

"Correspondances" 144

Cosmopolis 112

Coulon, Marcel 143

Coulouma 85

Coup de dés jamais n'abolira le hasard, Un 3, 112, 138

Courrier Sud 154

Courteline, Georges 112

Crastre, Victor 40

Crécy, Odette de 186

Crès, G. 108

"Crésus" 51

Crevel, René 40

Crimes de l'Amour, Les 16

Criterion, The 184

Croisset 91

Croix de bois, Les 72, 73

Cros, Charles 53, 111

Cubism 7, 14

Cummings, E. E. 3

Cunard, Nancy 33

Curtius, E. R. 84, 87

Dabit, Eugène 84

Dada, 3, 7, 13, 14, 75, 119, 120, 174

Dada 174

Dadaism 7

Dali, Salvador 36, 40, 69
Dali, Mme. Salvador 40
Dame à la faulx, La 158
damoiselle élue, La 63, 65
"dansemuses" 37
"Danses d'avant-garde" 95
"Dansez, montagnes" 52
Danville, Berthe 98
Daphnis et Chloé 106
Daragnès, Janine 72
Daragnès, Jean-Gabriel 15, 45, 57, 60–61, 72–73, 76, 79, 82, 95, 96, 100, 115, 121, 122, 140, 181
Darantière, Maurice 16, 37, 76, 121, 166, 167, 181
Darzens, Rodolphe 142
Daumal, René 36
Dauze, Pierre 29
Davray, Jean 29
Dayot, Armand 150
de Gaulle, General Charles. *See* Gaulle, General Charles de.
De la grandeur 100
De la musique encore et toujours 75
"De l'inutilité du théâtre au théâtre" 98
Debussy, Claude 57, 61, 63, 65–67, 69, 108
Dedicated to my Fiancée 15
Deharme, Lise 76
Delacroix, Eugène 14n, 27
Delaunay, Robert 10
Delahaye, Ernest 144
Delange, Cami 154
Delteil, Loÿs 139
Delcourt 76
Deman, Edmond 29
Demeny, Paul 142, 149
Demets, E. 164
Demont, Aglaé 158
Denis, Maurice 63, 65
Denoël, Robert 44, 179
Denoël et Steele 9, 175
Deplanche 72
Derain, André 9–10, 75, 125
Derème, Tristan 121
Derenne, Alphonse 111
Dermée, Paul 7, 14, 141
"Dernier voyage de Rimbaud, Le" 145
Dervois *fils* 97
Des Pensées inédites 91
Desbordes, Jean 58, 60, 84
Desbordes-Valmore, Marceline 184
Descamps-Scrive 184

Descaves, Lucien 76
Deschamps, Léon 148
Deslignières, André 75
Desnos, Robert 40
Desormière, Roger 162
Destin de Paris 102
Devauchelle, Roger 16
Devoir et l'inquiétude, Le 73, 75
Devoir, Le 75
Devoirs de vacances 135
Dévotion à la croix, La 42
Diaghilev, Serge 23, 69, 137, 162
Dianus. [Histoire de rats. (Journal de Dianus).] 27
Dial, The 184
Dialogues des inutiles 75
Dictionnaire abrégé du surréalisme 75
Diderot, Denis 27, 91
Diéterle, Jacques 113
Discours de Suède 42
Divoire, Fernand 13
Divagations 79
Divisionist technique 164
Dix portraits 92, 164
Doesburg, Theo van 120
"Don Juan aux enfers" 144
Dongen, Kees van 125
Dorbon-Aîné 69
Dorgelès, Roland 19, 72
Dornac 139, 185
Dos Passos, John 161
Dostoevski, Fyodor Mikhailovitch 183
"Dostoievsky d'après sa correspondance" 85
Doucet, Jacques 13
Dreier, Katherine 69
Drieu la Rochelle, Pierre 116
Drouin, Marcel 85
Druon, Maurice 159
Dubuffet, Jean 36, 122
Duchamp, Marcel 10, 69
Duchamp-Villon, Raymond 10
Dufour, Pierre. *See* Berrichon, Paterne.
Dufour-Rimbaud. *See* Berrichon, Paterne.
Dufy, Raoul 10, 72, 91
Duhamel, Georges 116
Dujardin, Édouard 75, 112
Dumas, Alexandre, *fils* 106
Dunoyer de Segonzac, André 72–73
Duncan, Isadora 151
Durand 137
Dutch colonial war registry 146
Dutch East Indian Army 146

Durey, Louis 57

"Earlier Visits to England" 182
Écho de Paris, L' 96
Éclair, L' 91
École d'Arcueil 164
École des femmes, L' 87
"Écrit sur la porte" 155
Écrits Nouveaux, Les 102
Édition du Mercure de France 96
Édition Russe de Musique 23
Éditions de la Fanfare de Montparnasse 121
Éditions de la Maison Française 154
Éditions de la Montagne 167
Éditions de la Nouvelle Revue Française 16,
    76, 79, 85, 87, 112, 130, 182
Éditions de la Revue Blanche 98
Éditions de la Sirène 57, 91, 135, 137
Éditions de Minuit, Les 32, 33
Éditions Denoël, Les 42
Éditions des Quatre Vents, Les 27
Éditions du Bélier 15
Éditions du Raisin, Les 37
Éditions du Siècle 116
Éditions Émile-Paul Frères 181
Éditions Eos 85
Éditions G. Crès, Les 122
Éditions Jeanne Bucher, Les 9
Éditions "Pro Francia" 175
Éditions *SIC* 12
"Effarés, Les" 184
Egorova, Madame 137
Ehrenburg, Ilya 84
Eliot, T. S. 3, 184
"Éloge III" 155
Éloges 155, 157
Éloges and Other Poems 157
Éluard, Paul 36, 39, 40, 54, 73, 75, 76, 88,
    122, 175
En attendant Godot 32, 33
En Sourdine 63
Enchanteur pourrissant, L' 9–10
Enfance de Pelléas, L' 69
Enfances 165
Enfant et les sortilèges, L' 23
"Enfer, L'" 95
Entr'acte 162
Entre centre et absence 116
Entretiens sur la politique 159
Épaves, Les 91
"Épuration d'une aube" 52
Erni, Hans 181

Ernst, Marie-Berthe 39
Ernst, Max 36, 39, 40, 75, 122
Espoir, L' 113, 115
Essai sur le naturisme 51
Essais critiques 159
Essor, L' 88
Estoppey, David 185
"Et maintenant, aux Fesses!" 185
Études pour "Mon Faust" 181
Eureka 182
Evans, Thomas W. 186
Eve 15
Everybody's Autobiography 129
"Examen, L'" 135
Ex-libris pour Guillaume Apollinaire 122
Exposition Internationale 75

F. F. ou le critique 122
"Façon" 37
"Fait divers" 140
Fantin-Latour, Ignace Henri Jean Théodore
    144
Fargue, Léon-Paul 76, 79, 162, 179
Fasquelle 124
Fauré, Gabriel 61
Faure-Favier, Louise 17
Faust 177, 187
Fautrier, Jean 122
Faux-monnayeurs, Les 85
Félix, Father 174
*Femme coiffée d'une toque et rejetant le
    buste en arrière* 138
*Femme de profil vers la gauche, coiffée d'un
    hennin* 138
Fénelon, François de Salignac de La Mothe
    101
Fénéon, Félix 112
Féquet et Baudier 181
Férat, Serge 12
Ferenczi 60
Fernande 124
Festival Claude Debussy 69
Festival Maurice Ravel 137
Festival of Angers 42
Festy, J. 59, 157
Fêtes Galantes 63
Feuilles de route 84
Figaro, Le 139
Figuière, Eugène 10
"Filet à papillons" 135
Filles du feu, Les 119
Firmin-Didot 138

Flaubert, Gustave 3, 88, 91, 139, 158
Fleuret, Fernand 113
Fleurs de Tarbes, Les 122
Fleurs du mal, Les 27–29, 91, 115
Floury, H. 73, 140
"Flûte de Pan, La" 65
Fontaine, Madame Lucien 65
Fort, Paul, 96
Fossombroni, Mme. Patersi de 104
Fourcade, Jacques 102
Fournier, Professor Alfred 186
Fournier, Dr. Edmond 186
Fourrier, Marcel 40
Fourmi dans le corps, La 20
France, Anatole 111
France, La 91
Franck, César 54, 104
Frénaud, André 122
French cathedrals 150
French Revolution 159
Frizeau, Gabriel 54
Fromont, Eugène 65
"Funeral Song for Théophile Gautier, A"
   111
Futurism 7, 14

Gabory, Georges 14, 174
Gaillard, Mme. 186
Gala (Helena Dmitrovnie Diakonova). *See*
   Dali, Mme. Salvador.
Gala Claude Debussy 67
Galère, La 83
Gallimard (Éditions) 27, 32, 37, 41, 42, 45,
   59, 81, 84, 93, 104, 155, 157, 181
Gallimard, Gaston 161
Gandon, Yves 41
Garden, Mary 66
Gaspard de la nuit 79
Gaubert, Philippe 69
Gaudeamus igitur 105
Gauguin, Paul 35, 49, 79–80, 112
Gaulle, General Charles de 180
Gauthier-Villars, Henri 61
Gautier, Théophile 34, 111
Gazette des Beaux-Arts, La 112, 134
Geffroy, Gustave 35, 93
Genet, Jean 81–83, 161
Geneviève ou l'École des Femmes 87
Genonceaux, L. 142
Géorgiques, Les 72
Gertrude Stein 167

*Gestes et opinions du docteur Faustroll, pata-
   physicien* 119
Ghil, René 100, 146
Gide, André 36, 57, 60, 84–85, 87–88, 112,
   122, 144, 155, 179, 181, 183
Gille, Dr. 105
Gilot, Françoise 129
Gindre, Caroline 148, 149
Gindre, Henriette 148, 149
Giraudeau, Germaine 130
Glatigny, Albert 111
Gleizes, Albert 10, 36
"Gloires" 57
Godet, Robert 92
Goethe, Johann Wolfgang von 14, 119
Gogh, Vincent van 49
Golaud 69
Goll, Yvan 174
Goncourt Academy 76, 93
Goncourt, Edmond de 88, 91
Gonne, Maud 187
Gonon, A.-J. 73, 75, 76, 79, 106
Gonzague-Frick, Louis de 75
Gorvel, Georges 150
Gosse, Edmund 111, 112, 182
Gounod, Charles François 104
Gourmont, Remy de 3, 91, 95, 142, 187
Grabinoulor 9
Gracq, Julien 40
Grains et issues 175
Granarius, Professor 24
Grand écart, Le 57–58
Grande Revue, La 85
Gras, Madeleine 72
Grasset, Bernard 60, 98, 100, 113, 130, 135
Grey, Madeleine 137
Grey, Roch 7, 17, 141
Grimace, La 15
Grindel, Paul-Eugène. *See* Éluard, Paul.
Gris, Juan 10, 40, 125
Grive, La 149
Gross, Valentine. *See* Hugo, Valentine
   (Gross).
Grove Press 32, 33
Guéhenno, Jean 116
Guérin, Marcel 80
Guignol's Band 42, 44
"Guillaume Apollinaire" 17

Hannotiau, Alexandre 29
Harcourt, Brace and Company 124, 166
Hartmann, Georges 65

Haute surveillance 81
Head of a Woman, face view 115
Head of a Woman, profile 115
Head of Isabelle Rimbaud 143
Hébert, Jacques-René 159
Hébertot, Jacques 42, 162
Hennequin, Émile 139
Hennique, Nicolette 145
Henry-Munsch, René 150
Héra. *See* Voilier, Jean.
Herbart, Pierre 60, 84
Herding, Louise 146
Hériat, Philippe 116
Hérissey, Charles 184
Hérold, A.-F. 97
Herrand, Marcel 14
Hessel, Helen 69
Hetzel 24
Heuzé, Edmond 96, 151
"Hiéroglyphe" 53
"Hirondelle" 135
Histoire de Bossuet, évêque de Meaux 101
Histoire de l'oeil 27
"Histoire du régent" 155
Homage to Apollinaire 15
Hombres 148
Hommage à Basket 125
Hommage à François Mauriac 116
"Hommage à Guillaume Apollinaire" 17
Hommes du jour, Les 91
Honegger, Arthur 57
Hôpital de la Conception 145
Hôtel Drouot 186
Huddleston, Sisley 42
Hugnet, Georges 27, 69, 76, 92, 162, 164–165, 167
Hugo, Jean 19, 20, 23, 135, 162
Hugo, Léopold 150
Hugo, Valentine (Gross) 20, 23, 39, 40, 51, 53, 59, 60, 76, 134, 135, 137, 162, 164
Hugo, Victor 23, 76, 107, 108, 111, 135, 150
Humanities Research Center 142, 148
Huser 84
Huysmans, Joris-Karl 93, 112, 186
Hypnerotomachia Poliphili 10

Ici la voix 92
Ides et Calendes 88
Idées du jour, Les 91
Ilg, Alfred 145
Illuminations, Les 142, 144
Illusion lyrique, L' 115

Illustrations 41
"Images à Crusoé" 155
"Imperméable, L'" 141
Impressionism 139
Impressionniste, L' 139
Imprimerie Darantière 58
Imprimerie Nationale 37
Imprimerie V. Vandersypen 84
"Inferno" 180
Inghelbrecht, D. E. 69
Innommable, L' 32, 33
"Institut de beauté" 135
"Introduction" 157
Introduction à la méthode de Léonard de Vinci 182
Introduction to the Method of Leonardo da Vinci 182
Ionesco, Eugène 4, 93
Isabelle 84, 85
Isabelle et Pantalon 23
Isabelle Rimbaud 143
Isabelle Rimbaud Reading by her Brother Arthur's Bed 143
"Iseum, L'" 119
Isis 119
Isis Vesper, Die 119
"Itinéraire (décrit) de mes personnages" 101
Izambard, Georges 142, 148–150
Izambard family 149

Jacob, Max 7, 23, 36, 95, 125, 129, 135, 140, 141
Jacob Cow le pirate, ou Si les mots sont des signes 122
Jacomet, Daniel 49
J'Adore 60
"J'ai connu à Daragnès" 61
Jaloux, Edmond 87
Jammes, Francis, 54, 84, 142
Jamot, Paul 73
Janco, Marcel 174
Japanese wood engravings. *See kwacho.*
Japanese woodcuts 35
Jarry, Alfred 4, 14, 35, 95–98, 119
"Je prends plaisir à m'étendre sur toi . . ." 7
"Je suis l'homme qui échoue" 76
"Je veux qu'on me donne des couleurs claires . . ." 9
"Jean Arp" 92
Jean-Aubry, G. 23, 137, 139, 162, 184

Jena Academic Festival Concerts 105
Jeune Parque, La 108, 181–183
Johnson, Una E. 51, 72, 140
Joie des sept couleurs, La 9
"Joseph Lebon" 159
Joues en feu, Les 135
Jouhandeau, Marcel 36, 37, 100, 113
Journal (André Gide) 88
Journal des Faux-monnayeurs, Le 85
Jouvet, Louis 84
Joyant, Maurice 169
Joyce, James 3, 16, 76, 101, 102, 120, 183
Juliette 16
Jusseaume, M. 66
"Juste présent" 175
Justes, Les 42
Justine 16

Kahn, Gustave 100, 142, 158
Kahnweiler, D.-H. 9–10
Keats, John 108
Khoklova, Olga. *See* Picasso, Olga Khoklova.
Kienerk, Giorgio 151
Kiki 69
Klee, Paul 36
Kra, Éditeur 150
Krohg, Lucy 121
Kunstmuseum (Berne) 15
kwacho 111
Kyrie 174

La Fayette, Mme. de 42
La Rochefoucauld, François, Duc de 42
La Sizeranne, Robert de 134
La Tour, Jean de 183
Labatut, Pierre 145
Lacretelle, Jacques de 116
Lafargue, Marc 51
Laforgue, Jules 3, 79, 100
Lagut, Irène 20, 135, 137
Lake, Carlton 129
Lamartine, Alphonse de 101, 135
Lamartine, Mme. Alphonse de 101
Lamballe, Lucienne 137
Lampe et les deux personnes, La 15
Lantier, Claude 51
Larbaud, Valery 76, 101–102, 120
Larivière, Jeanne. *See* Voilier, Jean.
Larousse 175
Last, Jef 84, 88
Launay 76
Laurencin, Marie 10, 122, 125

Laurens, Jean-Paul 84
Laurens, Paul-Albert 84
Laurent, Méry (Marie-Rose Louviot) 186
Le Blond, Maurice 51
Le Corbusier 102
Le Dantec, Yves-Gérard 107–108
Léautaud, Paul 122
Leblanc-Maeterlinck, Georgette 66, 69
Lebon, Joseph 159
Léda 98
Lefèvre, André 104
Legendre, M. 24
Léger, Alexis Saint-Léger. *See* Saint-John Perse.
Léger, Fernand 10
Léger, Saintléger. *See* Saint-John Perse.
Légion d'Honneur 151
Lehmann, Claude 20
Lehmann, John 84
Leiris, Michel 40, 102, 104, 122, 159
Lemerre, Alphonse 111
"Lendemain" 37
Leonardo da Vinci 182
Leroux 12
"Lettre du voyant" 149
"Lettre ouverte à M. Francis Jammes" 84
Lévy, Michel, Frères 27
Lhote, André 75
"Liberté-Égalité" 159
Librairie de l'Art Indépendant 63, 106
Librairie Gallimard 113, 155, 161
Librairie Stock 57, 130
Lièvre, Le 72
Life with Picasso 129
Lindon, Jérôme 32
Linossier, Raymonde 76, 79
Lisle, Leconte de 111
Liszt, Blandine. *See* Ollivier, Mme. Émile.
Liszt, Cosima. *See* Wagner, Mme. Richard.
Liszt, Franz 104–105
Liszt: The Artist as Romantic Hero 105
"Litanie d'eau" 41
Litanies de la mer. Invocations 158
"Litanies de Satan, Les" 28
Little Review, The 91
Livre blanc, Le 58
Livre d'art, Le 96
Livre des masques, Le 142
Lobstein 154
Lockspeiser, Edward 65
Losfeld, Eric 39
"Loup blanc" 157

Louÿs, Pierre, 63, 65, 66, 76, 106–108, 119 144
Loviton, Jeanne. *See* Voilier, Jean.
Luce, Maximilien 144
Lugné-Poe, A.-F. 95, 98
"Lumière Noire" 37
Luque, Manuel 184
Lurçat, Jean 75
Lust ou La Demoiselle de Cristal 177, 181
Lustig, H. G. 154
Luxembourg Garden 125

MacLeish, Archibald 157
MacOrlan, Pierre 121, 122
Madame Tussaud 19
"Madrigal" 37
Maeterlinck, Maurice 65–66, 67
Maeterlinck, Mme. Maurice. *See* Leblanc-Maeterlinck, Georgette.
Magritte, René 36
Maillol, Aristide 69
Maillol, Gaspard 58, 139
Maison des Amis des Livres, La 79, 185
Maison du berger, La 108
Maison Internationale des Pen-Clubs, La 41
Maîtres de l'Amour, Les 16
Making of Americans, The 164, 166–167
Malcorps 155
Mallarmé, Stéphane 3, 7, 19, 79, 80, 97, 111–113, 138, 142, 146, 157, 182, 184, 186
Malone Dies 32–33
Malone meurt 32–33
Malraux, André 113, 115, 122
Mamelles de Tirésias, Les 12–15, 19
Mapou, Charles 137
Manet, Édouard 79, 111
Manifeste du surréalisme 37
Manuel, Roland. *See* Roland-Manuel.
Marcel, Gabriel 81
Marcel Duchamp 69
Marchand, Léopold 9, 60, 61
Marché aux légumes, à Pontoise 140
Marche des polonais 96
"Marche funèbre" 120
Maré, Rolf de 162
Marion, Louise 13, 14
Marivaux, Pierre Carlet de Chamblain de 9
Marney, Thérèse 20
Martel, Jan 69
Martel, Joel 69
Martin, P.-L. 29, 95

Martin du Gard, Maurice 102
Martin du Gard, Roger 84, 116
Marx, Roger 112
Matarasso, H. 116
Mathot, Léon 81
Matinaux, Les 52
Matisse, Henri 13, 115, 124n, 125
Maubel, Renée 13
Maulnier, Thierry 116
Mauriac, François 88, 116, 183
Maurois, André 116, 161
Mauté de Fleurville, Mme. 63
McGraw-Hill Book Company 129
McGreevey, Thomas 182–183
Mercure de France 80, 91, 97, 98, 107, 134, 143, 144, 145, 149
Mercure de France 16, 95, 108, 130, 145, 148
"Médaillon avec cadres" 141
Médium, nouvelle série 39
Mélisande 66
Mellerio, André 138, 139
Mercher 102, 162
Meredith, George 182
Merle, Robert 159
"Mes Mémoires" 180
Messager, André 65–66, 69
Messaline 119
Metzinger, Jean 10
Meunier, Charles 28
Michaux, Henri 116, 122
Milhaud, Darius 23, 57, 76, 88
Milich, M. 87
Miller, Henry 3
Minotaure 37, 104
Miracle de la rose 83
Mirbeau, Octave 124, 164
Miró, Joan 36, 52, 92, 175
"Miserere" 151
Mobile 41
Molière 9, 107
Mollet, Jean 16
Molloy 32
Mon Faust 177, 179, 180, 181
"Mon Lou, ma chérie, je t'envoie aujourd'hui la première pervenche . . ." 16
Monde Libre, Le 37
Mondor, Professor Henri 111
Monet, Claude 49
Monfreid, Daniel 80
Monnier, Adrienne 75, 79, 102, 185
"Monôme" 53

Monsieur Teste 184
Mont de piété 37
Montesquiou, Robert, Comte de 134
Montfort, Eugène 72
Montherlant, Henri de 88, 116
Morale politique, Une 116
Moralités légendaires 79
Morand, Paul 116, 121, 155
Moreau, Claude 106
Morceaux choisis de la Fabrication des Américains 167
Morice, Charles 112, 185
Morin, Charles 96
Mornand, Pierre 72
Mort dans l'âme, La 161
"Mort de Guillaume Apollinaire, La" 174
Moulié, Charles 107
Mourlet 45
Mouvement Dada 174
"Mouvement naturaliste, Le" 88
Mur, Le 159
Murry, John Middleton 181
Muses, Les 55
"musique d'ameublement" 162
Musique, La 23
Musset, Alfred de 9

N. R. F. See Nouvelle Revue Française.
Nadar. See Tournachon, Félix.
Nadeau, Maurice 32
Napoléon III 186
National Education Ministry 113
Naturalist movement 88
Nausée, La 159, 161
Nef, La 39
Nemirovsky, Irène 116
Neo-Impressionist movement 164
Nerval, Gérard de 36, 79, 119, 158
Newman, John Henry 54
Nijinsky, Vaslav 59
Nin, Joaquin 137
Noailles, Charles, Vicomte de 75
Nobel Prize 42, 157
Non Vouloir 92
Nopalie 24
Nord-Sud 7
Norton, W. W. 157
"Note bibliographique" 157
"Note bibliographique sur les publications d'Éloges" 157
"Note 12 sur la poésie nègre" 174

"Note sur l'Affaire Gindre, pour être remise à Me. Amy, notaire" 149
Notes et contre-notes 93
Notes sur Bernard 79
Notre-Dame cathedral 54
Notre-Dame-des-Fleurs 82, 83
Nourritures terrestres, Les 84
"Nous sommes bien faits l'un pour l'autre" 185
Nouveau, Germain 148
Nouvelle Revue Française 57, 84, 85, 122, 130, 154, 155, 182
Nouvelles Littéraires, Les 102, 107, 157

Occident, L'. See Bibliothèque de l'Occident.
Ochsé, Louise 69
"Ode" 111
Odes en son honneur 184–185
Oeuvre du Marquis de Sade, L' 16
Oeuvre, L' 51
Oeuvres Complètes de Georges Bataille 27
Olivier, Fernande 124, 124n, 125, 130
Ollivier, Émile 104
Ollivier, Mme. Émile 104–105
Olympia Press 32
Ombre de mon amour 16
Ombiaux, Maurice des 84
Opéra (Paris) 137
Opéra-Comique 65–67
"Oraison du soir" 184
"Oreilles de Midas, Les" 149
Orestie, L' 27
Otto 134
Ouverture d'Ubu Roi 96
Ozenfant, Amédée 75

Palais de Chaillot 180
Paludes 84
Pan 76
Pan-pan au cul du nu nègre, Le 119
Pansa, Bianca da 119
Pansaers, Clément 119–120
Panthéon 180
Parade (Ballets Russes) 23, 162, 164
Parade (Rouault) 151
"Paradis, Le" 95
Parents terribles, Les 58–59
Paris le 5 mai 53 I 127
Paris le 5 mai 53 II 127
Par la taille 35, 97–98
Parler seul 175
Paroles en Espagne 116

Pascal, Blaise 54, 183
Pascin 121–122
Passion 151
"Passion, La. Les Clous du Seigneur" 95
Paul Verlaine 185
Paul Verlaine au Café François Ier 185
Paulhan, Jean 36, 37, 84, 88, 116, 122
"Pauvre Lélian" 184
Payne, John 111, 112
Pelléas 66
Pelléas et Mélisande 63, 65–66, 67, 69
Peintre-Graveur Illustré, Le 139
Peintres cubistes, Les. Méditations esthétiques. 10
"Peintres nouveaux, Les" 10
Pélican, Les 134
"pensefables" 37
"Pente" 141
Père Ubu. *See* Ubu.
Perényi, Eleanor 105
Péret, Benjamin 39, 40, 122
Pérey's Hotel 174
Perrin et Cie. 112
"personne de l'auteur n'appartient pas à son public, La" 157
"Pervigilium mortis" 107–108
Peter, René 63
Petit, Abbé Léonce 79
Petit Prince, Le 154–155
Petite surprise de jour de l'an 20
Petits poèmes parisiens 51
Phalange, La 119
Phanérogame, Le 95
"Phares, Les" 144
Philippe, Charles-Louis 72
Philosophie dans le boudoir, La 16
Pica, Vittorio 148
Picabia, Francis 7, 10, 120, 127, 162, 174
Picasso, Olga Khoklova 127, 129
Picasso, Pablo 10, 13, 14, 15, 16, 19, 23, 57, 93, 96, 122–125, 127, 129–130, 135, 162
Picasso, Paul (Paulo) 125, 127
Picasso 1930–1935 127
Picasso et ses amis 125, 130
"Picasso poète" 127
Pichon, Léon 75
Pierné, Gabriel 69
Pilote de guerre 154
Pino, Eloy 145
Pissarro, Camille 79, 139–140, 144, 164
Plain Edition 165, 167
Plaisirs et les jours, Les 130

Plan de l'aiguille, Le 46
Plautus, Titus Maccius 14
Plume, La 123
Poe, Edgar Allan 80, 181–182
"Poème anecdotique pour servir à l'histoire de notre temps" 14
"poème-paysage" 9
"Poèmepréfaceprophétie" 7
Poèmes 76
Poèmes, Les 158
Poèmes à l'autre moi 9
Poèmes inédits / Devoirs de vacances / Les Joues en feu 135
Poèmes pour la paix 75
"poésie pure, la" 182
Poète assassiné, Le 10
Poètes maudits, Les 184
Poétique 108
Point d'orgue / programmatique / pour jeune orang-outang 119, 120
"Poison perdu" 148
Poldès, Léo 15
Pollock, Jackson 41
Ponge, Francis 122
Pont Aven group 79
Pont de Londres, Le 42, 44
"Portrait" 141
Portrait de Cézanne 51
Portrait de Guillaume Apollinaire 19
Portrait de Léon-Paul Fargue 79
Portrait de Paul Verlaine 185
Portrait de Pierre MacOrlan 121
Portrait de René Char 53
Portrait de Renoir 140
Portrait de Rimbaud 150
Portrait de Tristan Derème 121
Portrait de Tristan Tzara 175
Portrait de Valentine Hugo 60
Portrait of Georges Auric 23
Poulenc, Francis 23, 24, 57, 76, 88
Poulet-Malassis, Auguste 29
Poulet-Malassis et de Broise 27
Pound, Ezra 3, 91, 120
"Pour la belle" 81
Pour la musique 79
Powell, York 112
Premier livre de Grabinoulor, Le 9
Premiers poèmes 75
Princeteau, René 169, 174
Prix Goncourt 76
Propos sur mon théâtre et sur les propos des autres 93

Proust, Marcel 59, 130, 134, 186
Proust, Mme. Adrien 134
Publications de La Vogue 100, 142
Puissances du désert, Les. See Voie Royale,
La.
Pur Jeudi 19

"Quand je cause avec toi paisiblement . . ."
185
Quantin 186
"quasi-poèmes" 180
"Quelques faits personnels" 116
"Qui l'ignorait?" 107
Quillard, Pierre 97

Rabelais, François 7
Rachel. *See* Voilier, Jean.
Rachilde (Mme. Alfred Vallette) 97, 98
Racine, Jean 9
Radiguet, Raymond 7, 19, 23, 59, 60, 134–
135, 137, 174
Random House 129
Rank, Madame Otto 9
Ravel, Maurice 23, 61, 137, 164
Ray, Man 69, 119
Raynaud, Ernest 148
"ready-made" 129
"Récolte injuriée, La" 52
Redon, Odilon 29, 113, 138–139
Réincarnations du Père Ubu, Les 151
Relâche 162
Reliquaire 142
Reliques 144–145
"Reliques, Les" 91
Reliquiae 145
"Remarques pour Maurice Martin du Gard"
102
Rempart de brindilles, Le 52
Renoir, Pierre-Auguste 91, 139–140
Renoir, Mme. Pierre-Auguste 139
Renoir et ses amis 140
Répertoire des pantins 96
Résurrection 119
Retour de l'U. R. S. S. 88
"Rêve du 22 mars 1938—6 heures du ma-
tin" 52
"Revenants futurs, Les" 92
Revenez vite Valentine 23
Reverdy, Pierre 7, 19, 120, 140
Révolution d'abord et toujours!, La 40
Revue du Siècle, La 116
Revue Indépendante, La 112

Reynal and Hitchcock 154
Ribemont-Dessaignes, Georges 13, 122
"Riche ventre qui n'a jamais porté" 185
Rien que la terre à l'exposition coloniale 121
Riès, Maurice 145
Righaz, Dimitri 145
Rimbaud, Arthur 19, 36, 54, 141–146, 148–
150, 184
Rimbaud, Frédéric 144
Rimbaud, Isabelle 142, 143, 144–145, 146,
148
Rimbaud, Léon 144
Rimbaud, Vitalie 145
Rimbaud, Mme. Vve. 143, 144, 145, 146,
149
Rimbaud 150
"Rimbaud catholique" 144
Rimbaud family 145
"Rimbaud mystique" 144
Rire d'un autre, Le 75
Rivière, Georges 139, 140
Rivière, Jacques 155
Rivière, Marcel et Cie. 85, 155
Robbe-Grillet, Alain 32
Robert ou l'intérêt général 84, 88
Robert. Supplément à l'École des Femmes
87
Robespierre, Maximilien François Marie Isi-
dore de 159
Robin, Albert 186
Rodin, Auguste 91, 112, 144, 150–151
Rodin 151
Rodker, John 182
Roerich, Nicolas 23
Roi Arthus, Le 54
Roland-Manuel 23
"Romance pour Colonna Romano, de la
Comédie-Française" 157
"Rome" 102
Ronsin 66
Rosenval, Karl 98
Rossetti, Dante Gabriel 63
Rouart, Eugène 84, 87
Rouart, Lerolle & Cie. 23
Rouault, Georges 151, 154
Rouault, Isabelle 151
Roujon, Henry 112
Rousseau, Henri (le douanier) 125
Roussel, Raymond 36, 60
Roux, Divine 158
Roux, Jacques 159
Ruche, La 15

Rue de Fleurus 92, 127
Rungis, Professor de 24
Ruskin, John 130, 134
Ruskin et la religion de la beauté 134

Sachs, Maurice 58, 179
Sachs, Maurice et Jacques Bonjean 58
Sacre du printemps, Le 23
Sagittaire 37
Saint-Exupéry, Antoine de 154–155
Saint-Exupéry, Comtesse Antoine de 154
Saint Genet, comédien et martyr 159
Saint-John Perse 54, 155, 157, 179
Saint-John Perse: Présentation par Alain Bosquet 157
Saint-Pol-Roux 157–158
St.-Sauveur-en-Puisaye 63
Sainte-Beuve, C.-A. 158
Saison en enfer, Une 19, 141, 142, 143
Salmon, André 7, 124n, 125
Salon de 1845 27
Salon de 1846 14n, 27
Salon de 1859 27
Salon des Indépendants 15, 35
Samazeuilh, Gustave 54
Sansot, E. 97
Santé, La 82
Sara 187
Sarrazin, Gabriel 63
Sartre, Jean-Paul 32, 122, 159, 161
"Sartre" 161
Satie, Erik 13, 23, 57, 63, 76, 162, 164
Saucier, Roland 161
Saül 84
Sautier, Marcel 96
Savouré, Armand 145
Sayn-Wittgenstein, Princess 104
Scandale aux abysses 45
Scènes de la vie privée et publique des animaux 24
Schiller, Johann 119
Schlumberger, Jean 116
Schneider, Jean-Georges 159
Schwabe, Carlos 29
Schwob, Marcel 95, 182
Seated Woman 115
Second Empire 170
Seconde, La 60–61
Segalen, Victor 144
Seghers 92, 157
Semet & Plumelle 51, 93
Serin muet, Le 13

Serpent, Le 72
Serrière, G. 108
Sert, Misia 23, 162
Sésame et les lys 130
Seurat, Georges 49, 79, 164
Shakespeare and Company 79
Shaw, George Bernard 91
Shelley, Percy Bysshe 108
SIC 7, 9, 14, 17, 19, 37, 141, 174
Signac, Paul 144, 164
Signac, Mme. Paul 144
"Signe de l'Ile de Pâques" 174
Sisley, Alfred 49, 139
Sivry, Charles de 142
Six, Les 57, 120
Skira, Albert 72
"Socialisme ou barbarie" 159
Socrate 13
"Socrate que j'ai connu, Le" 164
Soleillet, Paul 145
Solitaire ou les malédictions d'univers, Le 177, 181
Son, Idées, Couleurs. See *SIC.*
Sonatine pour le Piano 23
Sorbonne 93, 107
Sottiro, Constantinu 145
Souday, Paul 108, 183
Soupault, Philippe 7, 40, 150
Souvenirs de la maison des fous 175
Spanish Civil War 115
La Sphère de sable 92
"Splendeur humaine, La" 157
Stedelijk van Abbe-Museum, Eindhoven 15
Stendhal 27, 42, 91, 158
Stein, Gertrude 4, 92, 93, 124–125, 127, 164–167
Stein, Leo 124n, 125
Stern 174
Stevens, Alfred 63, 134
Stevens, Catherine 63
Stevens, Wallace 3
"Stratonice" 179
Stravinsky, Igor 23, 57, 59
Stroobants 184, 186
Stupra, Les 148
Suel, Jules 145
Sur la plage à Berneval 140
"Sur les monts les plus sauvages" 34
Surmâle, Le 119
Surrealism 4, 37, 75
Surréalisme au service de la révolution, Le 75

Sursis, Le 161
Survage, Léopold 14
Swann, Charles 59
Swinburne, Charles Algernon 111
Symbolism 88, 187
Symbolist drama 186
Symphonie pastorale, La. No. VII. Le Pasteur et Gertrude. 20

Tabourin 66
Tahitienne, La 115
"Taï de Camaret" 158
Tailleferre, Germaine 57
Tal Coat, Pierre, 167
Tancrède 76
Tanguy, Julien ("le père Tanguy") 49
Tanguy, Yves 36
Taoist philosophy 119
Tapié de Céleyran, Alix (sister-in-law of Adèle) 169
Tapié de Céleyran, Amédée (brother of Adèle) 170
Tapié de Céleyran, Louise (mother of Adèle) 169, 170, 174
Tapié de Céleyran, Mary (niece of Adèle) 169
Tartarin de Tarascon 72
Tchelitchev, Pavel 92
"Temple of Friendship" 108
Temps, Le 142
Temps du mépris, Le 113
Tentation de l'occident, La 113
Tentation de Saint-Antoine, La 139
Terrasse, Charles 140
Terrasse, Claude 35, 96, 97, 98
Terrasse, Mme. Claude 35
Terrain, Olympe 63
Tête d'enfant, de face, avec au-dessus un arc-en-ciel 138
"Tête de faune" 184
Tête de Paul 49
Thérèse 14
Théâtre Complet d'André Gide 88
Théâtre de l'Oeuvre 95, 96, 98
Théâtre de la Madeleine 61
Théâtre des Champs-Élysées 69, 162
Théâtre des Phynances 96
Théâtre du Châtelet 186
Théâtre Michel 60
Théâtre Municipal de Tunis 88
Theatre of the Absurd 134
Thibaud, Jacques 137

Thiele, Yvan 69
Third Republic 170
Thomas, René 20
Thomson, Virgil 164–165
391 3
Tian, César 145
Times (London) 181
Tirésias 14
"Toast funèbre" 111
Toklas, Alice B. 125, 129, 165, 166, 167
"Tombeau de Stéphane Mallarmé, Le" 157
Tombeau de Satie, Le 164
Tombeau de Théophile Gautier, Le 111
"Tombeau des Naïades, Le" 65
Toscanini, Arturo 69
Toulouse-Lautrec, Henri de 169–171, 173–174, 182
Toulouse-Lautrec Monfa, Adèle, Comtesse de 169–171, 174
Toulouse-Lautrec Monfa, Alphonse, Comte de 169–171, 173
Toulouse-Lautrec Monfa, Charles, Comte de 171
Toulouse-Lautrec Monfa, Gabrielle, Comtesse de (mother-in-law of Adèle) 169, 171, 174
Tournachon, Félix (Nadar) 28, 29
Tous les hommes sont mortels 32
"Transparents, Les" 52
Treille muscate, La 72
"13 études" 37
Triolet, Elsa 88
Trocadéro 180
Trois filles 121
3 petites filles dans la rue 122
Trois Roses, Les 37
Troubat, Jules 158
"Truite, La" 53
Tzara, Tristan 7, 32, 36, 69, 96, 120, 124n, 174–175

Ubu 95, 98
Ubu aux 4-z'arts 97
Ubu Enchaîné 97
Ubu Enchaîné précédé de Ubu Roi 98
Ubu Roi 35, 95–97, 98, 119
Ubu Roi ou les polonais 96
Ubu sur la butte 97
Ulysses 16, 76, 102
"Un dans l'autre, L'" 39
Un dans l'autre, L' 39
"universal mind" 182

University of Texas at Austin, The 3, 4
University of Upsala 42
Unnamable, The 32, 33

Vaché, Jacques 19
Valabrègue, Antony 51
Valéry, Jules 182
Valéry, Paul 3, 36, 107, 108, 122, 177, 179–184
Vallery-Radot, Robert 116
Vallette, Alfred 97, 98, 143
Vallette, Mme. Alfred. *See* Rachilde.
Vallier 49
van Dongen, Kees. *See* Dongen, Kees van.
van Gogh, Vincent. *See* Gogh, Vincent van.
Vanier, Léon 100, 185
Varèse, Louise 157
Vautier, M. 76
Vauvenargues, Luc de Clapier, Marquis de 42
Venturi, Lionello 51
Venus 129
Vénus du Gaz, La 129
Verbeke 76
Verlaine. Avril 1884, Café du Globe 185
Verlaine, Mathilde 63
Verlaine, Paul 3, 63, 91, 112, 142, 148, 184–185
Vermorel 184
Vernet, Horace 29
Vers et prose 112
"Vêtement du Prisonnier de Guerre, Le" 66
"Victoire éclair" 52
"Victor Hugo" 76
"Vie à Paris, La" 119
Vie de Jean-Arthur Rimbaud 142, 143, 148
Vienna Peace Conference 159
Vigny, Alfred de 108
Villa Bach 35
Village of Roche, The 143
Villard, Nina de 186
Ville-Evrard 20
Ville Ouverte 177, 181
Villiers de l'Isle-Adam, Jean-Marie Mathias Philippe Auguste, Comte de 112, 184, 186–187
Vinci, Leonardo da. *See* Leonardo da Vinci.
Vingt-deux artistes du livre 72
Vingt-et-un jours d'un neurasthénique, Les 124
"24 Juin 1917, Le" 19
"Vision" 116

Vlaminck, Maurice 19, 125
Vocabulaire 57
Vogue, La 142
Voie Royale, La 113
Voilier, Jean 177, 179–180, 181
"Voix de Marcel Proust, La" 134
Vollard, Ambroise 49, 72, 138, 151
Voltaire 116
von Bülow, Hans. *See* Bülow, Hans von.
Voûte, Paul 85
"Voyelles" 184
Vuillermoz, Émile 46, 60, 61, 66, 67, 69, 113, 137, 154, 164

Wagner, Richard 104, 119, 179
Wagner, Mme. Richard 104–105
Waiting for Godot 32, 33
Warnod, André 122
Watt 32
Weil, Simone 36
Weill, Berthe 13
Weingartner, Paul Felix 69
Welcome Hotel 23
Wharton, Edith 59
Whibley, Charles 184
Whistler, James Abbott McNeill 112
Whitman, Walt 91, 101
Wilder, Thornton 129
Willy. *See* Gauthier-Villars, Henri.
Willy, Colette. *See* Colette.
Wind Among the Reeds, The 187
Wols 122
Woolf, Albert 139
Woolf, Virginia 161
World War I 144
World War II 32, 88

Xiemeas. *See* Voilier, Jean.

Yack, Dan 46
Yeats, William Butler 3, 4, 187
Yerta-Méléra, Marguerite 145
"Yeux doux, Les" 57
Ymagier, L' 95
Yseux, successeur de Thierry-Simier 112

Zervos, Christian 122
Zeus 15
Zimmerman, Ernest 145
Zola, Émile 46, 51, 91
Zola, Mme. Émile 46

AFTERWORD

The idea for this exhibit originated with Dr. Warren Roberts, Director of the Humanities Research Center, and without his continuing enthusiasm and support it would not have come to fruition. Throughout my work on it I have had assistance from many of his associates and I should like to thank all those who helped make the job as enjoyable as it proved to be. I owe a special debt of gratitude to Mrs. Sally Leach, Assistant Librarian, whose buoyant good spirits, shrewd insights, and practical solutions to a variety of problems were of transcendent value.

C. L.

A NOTE ON THE AUTHOR

Carlton Lake has had a lifelong involvement with France and the French— in particular with French art and literature, about which he has written books and articles from Paris over the past twenty-five years. A collector of books and manuscripts, he bought his first major French book as an undergraduate nearly forty years ago when he acquired, at the Harry B. Smith Sale, No. 52 of the present catalogue.

This volume has been printed on Nekoosa Natural.
The type is Linotype Caledonia for the text with Monotype
Perpetua for the titling. Design by William R. Holman